TABLE of CONTENTS

PREFACE

This book originated as a series of 24 articles which were printed in the *Sports Turf Manager*, a publication of The Sports Turf Association of Ontario. The book brings under one cover, with some updating, the information contained in those articles, the first of which was published in 1991.

It must be emphasized that the concepts contained herein are equally applicable to all sport facilities using turf, whether they are golf greens or race tracks for thoroughbreds. Therefore, it may be of equal value to the golf superintendent as to the turf manager employed by a municipality.

You have just purchased your personal copy of "Understanding Turf Management." What do you plan to do with it? Do you plan to place in on the shelf with other books you own as a trophy to influence visitors? Or, do you plan to read it, place it on your desk, with tagged sections, soiled with dirty hands and share it with your fellow workers. The author hopes the latter is the case.

May the knowledge contained herein improves your position as a turf manager or golf superintendent. Knowledge, however, is a never-ending process. So use this book as a base for further reading and understanding turf management.

Sheard, R.W., 1927-

Understanding Turf Management

Includes index.

ISBN 0-9686568-0-3

1. Turf Management 2. Turfgrasses. I. Sports Turf Association (Guelph, Ont.)

II. Title

SB433.S53 2000 635.9'642 C00-930368-S

Production/Design by Willustration, Guelph, Ontario

Cover photo by Donald J. Hamilton

Printed and bound by Moffitt Print Craft, Guelph, Ontario

ACKNOWLEDGMENTS

The author is indebted to all those turf managers who listened to his lectures about turf and responded, both favourably and critically, to his words. That interchange of ideas has resulted in this book which serves as a means of passing on those discussions to others. The author must also acknowledge the authors of other volumes on turf management whose writings have in many ways influenced this volume.

Specifically the author expresses his appreciation to Prof. Jack Eggens, Dr. Ken Carey and Ms. Pam Charbonneau for information and comments during the preparation of several articles which were the basis of the book.

CHAPTER 1

THE SOIL

The primary functions of the turf manager are to mow the grass, provide protection against insects and disease, eliminate undesirable species and correct the soil conditions to those which optimize grass growth. Since the grass must be growing vigorously before the other management functions become relevant, the logical place to begin an understanding of turf management is with the soil on which the grass grows.

A soil in its natural state is the end product of centuries of time, the climate, the vegetation resulting from that climate and the original geological material at the site. The natural soil exhibits the interaction of these factors through the formation of layers, called soil horizons.

The management of soil is among the oldest of arts, but none is changing more rapidly. We know more about taking care of the soil than our fathers or grandfathers, yet there is much more we should know.

(Ezra Taft Benson, U.S. Secretary of Agriculture, 1957)

Soil Horizons

In their natural state the horizons of a soil are easily visible to the observer (Fig. 1.1) The uppermost horizon is called the "A" horizon which the layman commonly refers to as topsoil (Fig. 1.2). It may vary in depth from 10 to 30 cm. It is relatively dark

Figure 1.1: The profile of a sandy loam soil in Southern Ontario in its original state.

Figure 1.2: The relationship between the horizons of a natural soil and a constructed soil.

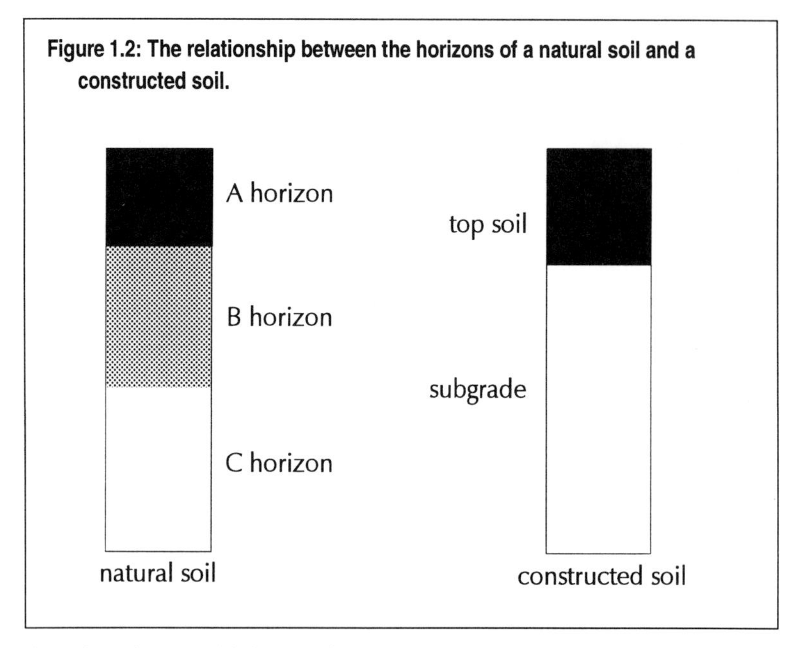

in colour due to a high organic matter content, more fertile and has superior soil structure or tilth to that of lower depths. It contains the highest concentration of plant roots.

The transition zone between the "A" horizon and lower depths from which the soil developed is the "B" horizon. It may be 15 to 45 cm in depth. This zone has significantly less organic matter and fertility and poorer structure. As a result it is more difficult to till and the layman refers to it as subsoil.

The lowest layer is known as the "C" horizon, commonly called the parent material. It has not been changed by time, climate and vegetation. It contains no organic matter, has poor to no soil structure and low fertility. In most Canadian soils it has a high pH. To many this zone is known as the subgrade.

Most soils used for the production of turfgrass do not have the natural sequence of "A", "B", and "C" horizons. During the construction process the "A" horizon, and probably part of the "B" horizon is stripped and stockpiled. Surface grading blends the remaining "B" horizon and the "C" horizon together (note the uneven surface of the "C" horizon in Figure 1.1) to which the mixed "A" and "B" horizons are reapplied or a new soil material is introduced. Thus the soil on which turf is generally produced does not have the attributes of a natural soil, but must be considered a constructed soil of some depth of top soil, which may also have been modified by the process of stripping and replacement, overlying the subgrade.

Functions of Soil

The first function of a soil is to provide an anchor for the roots of the plants. Anchorage is dependent on the depth of grass rooting and density of the roots in the soil.

Anchorage may not seem important for such a low growing plant, but the anchorage provided by the roots in the soil is very important in athletic turf. The turf must be well anchored to prevent the turf from being torn loose by the short turns and sudden stops of the players. A field built on a sand base is particularly susceptible to this damage if put into play before the grass has fully developed a root system. Likewise a newly sodded or seeded field is subject to the same damage.

The second function of the soil is to provide the three essential ingredients for optimum grass growth. They are plant nutrients, water and air.

With the exception of carbon from the carbon dioxide in the atmosphere, all of the elements required for grass growth are obtained from the mineral material and organic matter in the soil. The water absorbed by the root system comes from the soil. Furthermore, the elements in the soil that the plant requires for growth must be dissolved in the soil water before they can be taken up by the grass. Air is necessary in the soil to allow the root system to exchange oxygen and carbon dioxide in the process of respiration, the essential life process in plants as well as in animals.

The air and water in the soil are found in the pore spaces, those cavities between the solid particles. A perfect soil would contain 50% pore spaces and 50% solid material on a total volume basis (Fig. 1.3). Through the intricate formation of the soil structure, however, such a porous material is still supportive of great weights, i.e., tractors and mowing equipment.

The solid portion of the soil has two components, organic matter and minerals. Only 2.0 to 2.5% of the total volume of the soil may be

Figure 1:3: The relationship between soil minerals, organic matter, air and water under ideal, saturated and compacted soil conditions.

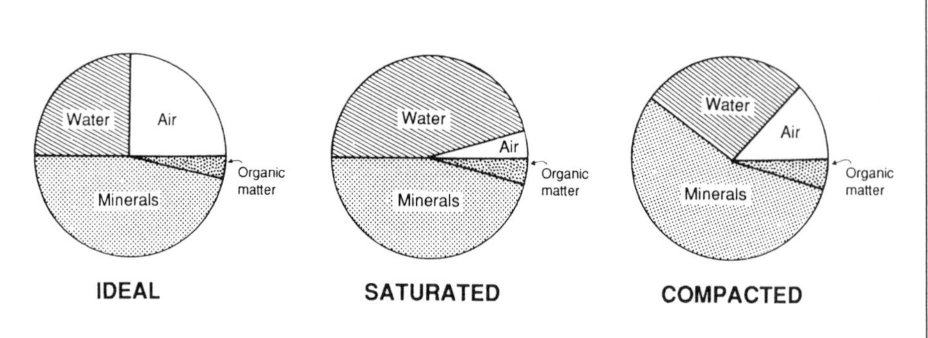

organic matter, however, it is so vital to the growth of grass that its importance to soil properties and turf growth far exceeds the small proportion found in the soil. The remainder of the solid portion is mineral material ranging in size from the smallest clay particles, only observed in photographs taken by electron microscopes, to stones and gravel. It is the mineral material in the soil which provides most of the elements the grass requires for growth.

The pore space or empty space between mineral particles is occupied by air and/or water. In the perfect soil half of the space would contain air and half would contain water. As the soil dries more and more of that space becomes filled with air, whereas when the soil becomes wetter the soil pores contain less and less air. Eventually the soil would contain no air, a condition known as a waterlogged or poorly drained soil.

Because the soil contains little air when it is saturated with water, normal root respiration is reduced. Without respiration uptake of plant food is slow and in turn plant growth is retarded. If this condition is allowed to persist in sports fields, a shallow root system develops, reducing the anchorage of the turf. The relationship between soil water and soil air is the reason why an adequate drainage system is essential in a sports field and compaction must be controlled.

In a well-aerated soil the composition of the air is similar to that of the atmosphere which is 79% nitrogen, 20.9% oxygen and .03% carbon dioxide. Normally the soil has slightly higher carbon dioxide levels than the atmosphere. Within 48 hours of the soil becoming saturated with water, however, the concentration of carbon dioxide increases and the amount of oxygen decreases sharply. The soil is now said to be anaerobic [lacks oxygen] in contrast to a normal or aerobic soil. In addition other gases such as methane and ethylene begin to be formed. Ethylene, at low concentrations, acts as a plant hormone, interfering with normal plant growth.

The aeration of the soil is also decreased by compaction. Continued traffic, particularly when the soil is excessively wet, causes the soil particles to move closer together. The water actually facilitates the process, acting as a lubricant for the movement of soil particles. When compaction occurs, the larger pores are compressed first. These larger pores are important in the free transfer of gases in and out of the soil. Similarly the rapid movement of excess water from the soil is dependent on the larger pores.

Compaction also increases the physical force the root must exert to penetrate the soil. Experiments have shown, however, that if adequate oxygen is provided the physical limitation is greatly reduced, indicating the first limitation to root growth in compacted soils is aeration.

Thus the soil, whether natural or constructed, is a dynamic system of soil particles and open space containing of air and water. The maintenance of the optimum relationship among the three components is the objective of the turf manager.

CHAPTER 2

SAND, SILT and CLAY

Soil Separates

The mineral fabric of soil is the product of geological degradation of the rock exposed at the soil surface; relatively uniform if degraded from in situ rock, complex if transported from many surfaces by wind or water.

Any sample of soil is made up of a continuous array of particles which range from the smallest clay particles to large gravel. In order to describe soils, scientists have established a classification system for a range of particle sizes; size ranges which reflect their observed role in many of the familiar soil properties. The classification system divides the particles into four classes - gravel and stone, sand, silt, and clay. Table 2.1 lists the Canadian classification system for the size range of particles which may be found in a soil sample. Each size range is known as a soil separate and has been assigned a specific name, i.e., clay, silt, fine sand, gravel.

The scientists have assigned the name "clay" to the finest particles, and not without reason. Clay size particles are the source of most of the chemical properties of soil. They are responsible for the retention of many of the plant nutrients in the soil, such as calcium, magnesium, potassium, the trace elements and some of the phosphorus. Clays react with the breakdown products of organic matter to stabilize the organic matter as humus in the soil. A soil without clay particles can be a very infertile soil.

Clays, because of their very small size and very large surface area (Table 2.1), are able to retain greater amounts of water than sandy soils. On the other hand, as will be discussed in Chapter 4, clays hold the water more closely and do not release the water as readily to grass roots as sands. Clay particles have a vastly greater tendency to stick together than sand, and it is common farmer knowledge that soils high in clay are difficult to till. When a small sample of a clay soil is wetted and rubbed between the fingers it will feel very sticky and is easily rolled into a string.

Table 2.1: The classification system for soil particles; their sizes, surface area and visibility.

Soil Separate	Size Range	Surface Area	Visibility
	(mm)	(cm^3/gm)	
Clay	less than .002	23,000	electron microscope
Silt.	.002 to .05	2,100	light microscope
Very fine sand	.05 to .10	2,000	light microscope
Fine sand	.10 to .25	210	human eye
Medium sand	.25 to .50	—	
Course sand	.50 to 1.0	21	
V. course sand	1.0 to 2.0	—	
Gravel	2.0 to 100	—	
Boulders	larger than 100	—	

The particles classified as "silts" are intermediate in size. They have chemical and physical properties in between clay and sand. The silt particles have limited ability to retain plant nutrients, or to release them to the soil solution for plant uptake. Silt tends to have a spherical shape, giving a high silt soil a soapy or slippery feeling when rubbed between the fingers when wet. It is more difficult to roll into a string than clays.

Because of the spherical shape, silt also retains a large amount of water, but silts releases the water readily to plants. Whereas silt soils are generally considered very productive, largely due to their water characteristics and ease of cultivation, engineers dread working with them due to their relatively easy release of water and the lack of ability of the silt particles to stick together.

Sand particles are essentially small rock fragments, and as such, have little or no ability to supply grass with nutrients or to retain them against leaching. As rock fragments, sandy soils feel gritty between the fingers. The sand grains have little ability to stick together; thus sandy soils cannot be rolled into a string when wetted.

It is well known that sandy soils are droughty soils because they retain little water when wetted. Nevertheless what water is retained is easily released to plants. When rain or irrigation occurs the water readily penetrates the soil surface, the excess moves through rapidly and the soil remains well aerated. These properties make sands a desirable medium for growing sports turf where there is no limitation in applying water and nutrition, as needed, throughout the season.

Particle Size Distribution

The analysis for the distribution of the various particles in a soil sample (particle size analysis) of the sand portion is conducted using a set of screens which have mesh sizes that retain the various ranges of sand particles. Estimating the silt and clay is more complicated as it requires measuring the rate of settling of the particles in water. The analysis is based on a law of physics which states that small diameter particles settle more slowly in water than larger diameter particles. By dispersing a sample of soil in a column of water, where it is assumed that all particles settle independently of each other, and taking samples at predetermined depths and time intervals, the technician can calculate how much silt and clay is contained in the soil.

Because there can be an infinite array of percentages of sand, silt and clay in soils, scientists have devised a procedure for classifying the potential combinations into 12 groups which reflect broad soil properties. These groups are called textural class names and are obtained by applying the particle size analysis to a textural triangle (Fig. 2.1). Thus a soil which contains 40% sand, 40% silt and 20% sand would be called a loam soil. Table 2.2 lists several textural class names and a typical particle size distribution for each.

Table 2.2: Some typical particle size analysis and the corresponding textural class name.

Particle Size Analysis			
Sand	**Silt**	**Clay**	**Textural Class Name**
—% by weight——			
61.0	28.0	11.0	Sandy Loam
40.0	41.0	19.0	Loam
20.0	61.0	19.0	Silt Loam
28.5	42.0	31.0	Clay Loam

Fig. 2.1: The textural triangle used for assigning textural class names. (A straight line drawn along the grid for the percentage clay and for the percentage silt will intersect within a class name area).

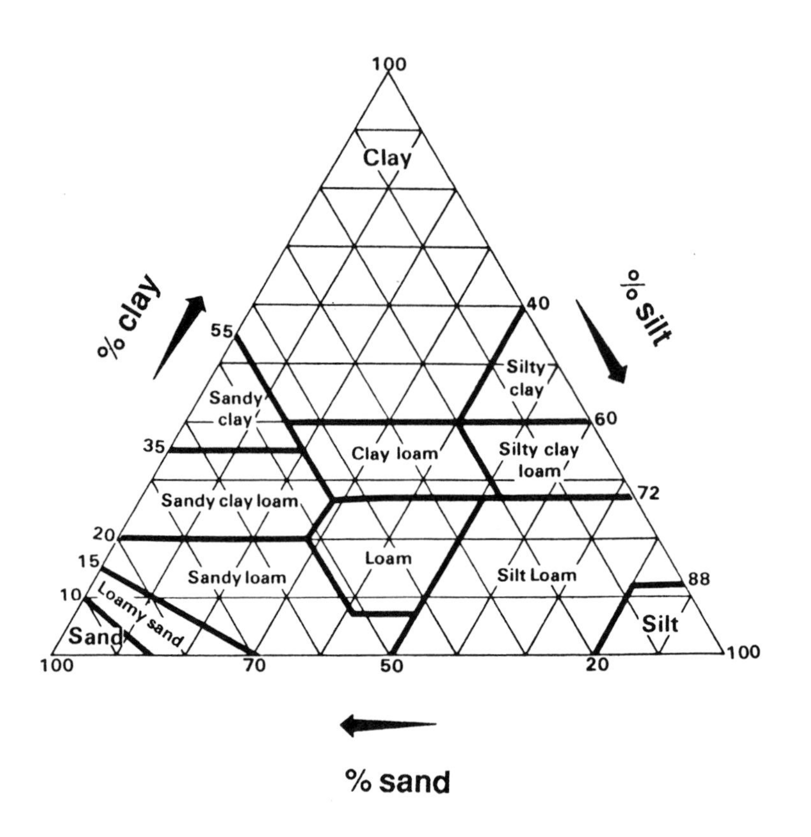

Some confusion occurs between turf managers and the soil scientist in the use of these terms. The soil scientist considers the name loam or clay to refer to a range of particle sizes in a soil. The turf manager often refers to a loam as a soil which is easy to till or is not compacted whereas a clay is difficult to work, is compacted, or may even be a subsoil which is difficult to work because it lacks organic matter. Errors in resolving the cause of some turf management problems can result from the conflicting interpretation of the names used for textural class and particles size distribution. A laboratory analysis should be the precursor of investigating these problems.

In summary, many chemical and physical properties of a soil can be assessed in rough terms from a knowledge of a particle size analysis or the textural class name. For example, in comparing a clay to a sandy loam it can be expected that,

1) the clay will be relatively more fertile,
2) the clay will have greater nutrient holding capacity for potassium, calcium and magnesium,
3) the clay will have more organic matter,
4) the clay will hold more plant available water and to be less subject to drought,
5) the clay will have smaller pores resulting in slower air and water movement within the soil, and
6) the clay will have greater stickiness, ability to retain a shape when moulded, and be harder when dry.

CHAPTER 3

SOIL STRUCTURE, DENSITY and POROSITY

Structure is a phenomenon of most natural surface soils, but it is totally absent from sand based rooting systems. In natural soils structure influences density and porosity; in sand based systems particle size distribution dictates density and porosity.

If the mixture of sand, silt and clay particles in the soil remained separated as individual particles the smaller particles of clay and silt would migrate into the holes between the larger sand fragments to create a dense material such as found at depth in the C horizon of a normal soil. An analogy would be to take a bin of softballs, fill the bin with marbles, shake it till no more marbles can be added, then add SCU pellets until no more of them can be added. This simulation would have little porosity and is analogous to a dense, compacted soil.

Such a soil would be a very poor medium for root growth as it would have little air or water movement and great resistance to root penetration. Good turf management requires the use of cultural practices which will help to reverse this situation.

Soil Structure

Fortunately, under normal circumstances, soil particles tend to group together into larger, semipermanent arrangements known as aggregates (clods, peds, crumbs). The result of aggregation is called soil structure. Simply stated, the importance of soil structure is it tends to make soils which are high in clay act like sand in terms of air and water movement. A comparison of a typical water stable aggregate analysis on to the textural class name of the size ranges of sand is illustrated in Table 3.1.

Table 3.1: A comparison of a typical water stable aggregate analysis with the textural class names of sand.

Aggregate Size Range	Water Stable Aggregates	Sand Class Name
(mm)	(%)	
<.05	0.0	clay & silt
.05 - .10	4.8	very fine sand
.10 - .25	10.2	fine sand
.25 - .50	30.7	medium sand
.50 - 1.0	28.9	coarse sand
1.0 - 2.0	16.4	very coarse sand
2.0	9.0	gravel

There are a number of factors influencing the ability of a soil to establish a stable soil structure. The primary factor is soil organic matter. The breakdown products of organic matter create a cementing effect which hold the mineral particles together. Calcium, iron and the type of clay also have a positive effect on structure formation.

It is necessary, however, to move the particles close together before the cementing action can become effective. The movement of particles closer together is brought about through root action, soil insects such as earthworms, freezing and thawing, and wetting and drying of the soil.

Of prime importance in the evaluation of soil structure is the stability of the aggregates, which is the resistance to disintegration under the destructive forces of wind, rain, vehicle and foot traffic; the latter two being the forces of concern for turf. Aggregate stability is very closely related to the amount and type of organic matter present.

Of all plant species grass provides the most effective means of promoting stable soil structure. Nevertheless under continued traffic, particularly when the soil is kept excessively moist through poor drainage or excessive irrigation, the structure can be destroyed and the soil will become compacted.

Soil structure is of primary importance where the soil contains more than 15% silt and clay. Soil structure, however, is not a factor in sport fields constructed on sand-based root systems because sands will not form aggregates. The selection of the correct size distribution of sands is used as a substitute for soil structure. The selection is critical to prevent migration of fine sand particles into the spaces between the larger sand grains, creating a low porosity root zone.

Soil Density

The degree of compaction of a soil is measured by determining the bulk (apparent) density of the soil. The determination is a simple procedure, involving the insertion of a small (5-cm diam. by 2-cm deep) ring into the soil. The ring is carefully excavated, trimmed level at the top and bottom and dried for 48 hours at 105 C. The bulk density is the dry weight (grams) of the soil in each cubic centimetre of volume.

The volume of dry soil in the ring includes both the solid mineral particles and the spaces between the particles, that is, the porosity. The more compacted a soil the greater the density. Thus, the greater the weight of soil particles compressed into each cubic centimetre and the smaller the air spaces (Table 3.2).

Table 3.2: The relationship between compaction, apparent density and porosity.

Degree of Compaction	Apparent Density	Total Porosity	Macro Porosity	Micro Porosity
	(gm/cm3)	(%)	(%)	(%)
Low	1.31	50.5	21.5	29.0
Medium	1.49	43.7	15.8	27.9
High	1.64	38.1	10.9	27.2

Soils may vary in density from 1.0 to 1.95 gm/cm^3. The ideal soil, as described in the first chapter as having a total pore space of 50%, would have a density of 1.32. Natural soils with greater densities than 1.55 can be considered to have serious compaction problems. Root zones constructed with a high proportion of the correct distribution of sand particles, however, can be expected to have a density as high as 1.65, while still retaining good root penetration and air and water characteristics.

Soil Porosity

The first chapter described the relationship between mineral and organic material, air and water. The air and water in the soil existed in the pore space in the soil. Thus, an understanding of soil porosity is a further step in understanding good turf management.

The sizes of the pores have an infinite range from submicroscopic between silt and clay particles to the very large pores visible to the eye which are formed by earthworms and decaying root channels — commonly called bio-pores. For this discussion the pore sizes may be divided into two broad groups — macro pores, and micro pores.

Analytical techniques exist which permit the assessment of the relative percentage of each group of pores in a soil sample. The total porosity may be calculated directly from the density measurements. This single value, however, says nothing about the size of the pores which is important in air and water movement.

$$\text{Percent total pore space} = 100 - \frac{\text{Bulk Density}}{2.65} \times 100,$$

where 2.65 is the average density of the soil particles only.

Laboratory techniques, which give an assessment of the relative size of the pores is based on the amount of water retained in the soil in a container, such as the ring described above, when it is placed in a special apparatus to which suction can be applied. The suction applied is representative of certain moisture conditions which exist in the field.

When the soil is saturated with water 100% of the pores are filled with water, thus the total pore space equals the volume of water in a measured volume of soil at this water content. If the soil is allowed to drain freely in the field until all of the water that will flow out due to the pull of gravity has occurred the macro pores will be empty. The volume of the macro pores will equal the volume of water lost. The micro porosity is equal to the volume of water remaining in the soil at this stage. It may be determined by drying a sample of the soil for 48 hours at 105 C. Since the micro porosity plus the macro porosity equals the total porosity, the macro porosity is then determined by subtraction of the percent micro porosity from the total porosity.

Macro porosity (non-capillary porosity or aeration porosity) is important in the rapid drainage of excess water from the soil after heavy rain or excessive irrigation. Rapid removal of this water allows the air essential for root function to return to the soil.

Micro porosity (capillary porosity) retains the water required for plant growth. The micro pores will also become filled with air as the grass extracts the water from the soil. The water in the micro pores is not lost by the forces of gravity. The smaller the pores, however, the greater the difficulty the plant experiences in extracting the water. Hence the grass will show moisture stress before all the capillary pores are empty. To prevent moisture stress irrigation should occur when 50 percent of the capillary pores are empty.

Compaction results in a reduction in the number, size and continuity of the soil pores. Initially the macro pores will be destroyed (Table 3.2), reducing the rate of water infiltration and the drainage ability of the soil, the aeration of the soil and the ability of roots to penetrate the soil. The lack of oxygen further reduces the grass roots' ability to penetrate the soil.

The greater the moisture content of a soil the more easily it can be compacted because the water acts as a lubricant allowing the particles to move into closer arrangements. Therefore, avoidance of excessive irrigation and the improvement of surface and internal drainage will assist in avoiding compaction.

Fortunately the grass ecosystem is recognized as the optimum system for promoting soil structure. As a result the apparent density of the soil will be reduced, increasing the porosity of the soil, particularly the macro porosity. Using cultural practices which favour vigorous root growth, combined with adequate drainage and good water management are the best preventative systems against compaction.

CHAPTER 4

SOIL AIR AND WATER

In the previous chapter soil porosity and the relationship between water and air in the soil pores was discussed. In summary, as the soil dries, more and more of the soil porosity become filled with air, whereas when the soil is wetted by rain or irrigation the air is forced out of the pores as they refill with water.

Without air to breathe and water to drink man does not survive. Likewise a grass root requires the same essentials of life. Good management of the soil provides each in the optimum proportions.

Soil Air

During the process of wetting and drying there is an exchange of the air between the soil and the atmosphere. In addition there is a continued exchange of air due to a second process called diffusion; a much slower, but continuous, process. Furthermore the air may move in and out of the soil due to expansion from the heating of the soil during the day.

In an inactive soil without plants the concentration of gases in the soil is the same as that in the atmosphere we breathe — 21.0% oxygen, 0.03% carbon dioxide, 78.9% nitrogen and the remainder a mixture of other gases. When grass roots grow in the soil or when the microbial population is active, respiration, a process which takes place within all living cells, occurs. During respiration oxygen is consumed and carbon dioxide is produced. Without continued exchange of gasses between the soil pores and the atmosphere, a level of oxygen will be reached, generally less than 10 percent, where respiration is reduced and the roots will die.

When a soil is close to saturation with water the time required for the soil to become depleted in oxygen is reduced to one or two days. The soil is now known as anaerobic (lacks oxygen) in contrast to an aerobic (normal) soil. Thus, good drainage is essential to maintain an aerobic soil. Compaction, which tends to disproportionately destroy macro pores, also results in reduced gas diffusion and a low oxygen level in the soil.

As the oxygen in the soil is depleted by the process of respiration, the carbon dioxide level is increased. When the carbon dioxide level approaches three to five percent it will become toxic to the root system of grasses. To further intensify the harmful effects of low oxygen on grass roots in an anaerobic soil, microbes which do not require oxygen multiply and in their respiration process produce gasses such as ethylene which are toxic to plant growth at very low levels, levels measured in a few parts per million.

An additional adverse effect of a decreasing oxygen supply in the soil is a change in the oxidation state or physical chemistry of the soil. Anaerobic soils develop what is called "reducing" conditions which increases the iron and manganese concentration in the soil solution to a level which may also be toxic to root development. Furthermore, nitrogen, a critical plant nutrient, may be lost as a gas to the atmosphere by a process called denitrification.

Soil Water

While excessive water in the soil may be harmful, an adequate supply of water in the soil micro pores is essential at all times for grass growth. There are three basic functions of the water in the soil,
(1) to replace the water lost through evapotranspiration from soil and leaf surfaces,
(2) to act as a solvent in which all plant nutrients must dissolve before they are absorbed by the grass roots, and
(3) to act as a moderator of soil and leaf temperatures. The moderating effect is due to the requirement for at least five times more energy to raise the temperature of water one degree Celsius than the temperature of soil or leaf tissue.

Water, even in the driest soil, exists as a layer over the surface of all soil particles. This layer increases in thickness as the soil becomes more moist. Eventually, as the water content increases further, the smallest pores become filled with water first, followed by larger and larger pores (Fig. 4.1).

Water is held in the soil by physical forces of adhesion and cohesion. These forces create a tension or "pull" on the water so that energy is required to remove the water or counteract this tension. The thinner the layer of water on the soil particles the greater the energy that must be exerted to remove the water. Hence, a point is reached where the grass root cannot exert enough energy to extract water and the plant wilts. Conversely, as the soil becomes more moist the energy the root must exert to obtain its water requirement decreases.

Soil scientists have developed a system of defining the energy required to remove the water from the soil. They have established a reproducible laboratory procedure which relates the moisture content of the soil to the energy or tension, in units of bars, by which the soil retains water. The procedure generates what is called moisture retention curves (Fig. 4.2). These curves illustrate two points. The first point is a sandy soil contains less water at any given energy level than a clay. The second, and more important point is the amount of water held between any two energy levels is less in the sand than in the clay. The difference between sands and clays is due to the greater number of fine particles in clay soils and the greater surface area associated with these fine particles.

Figure 4.1: A schematic representation of water, air and soil particles. On the left is a dry soil at the permanent wilt point. On the right is a saturated soil where air remains only as small pockets between the particles. Some of this water will drain out of the soil, drawing fresh air into the pores.

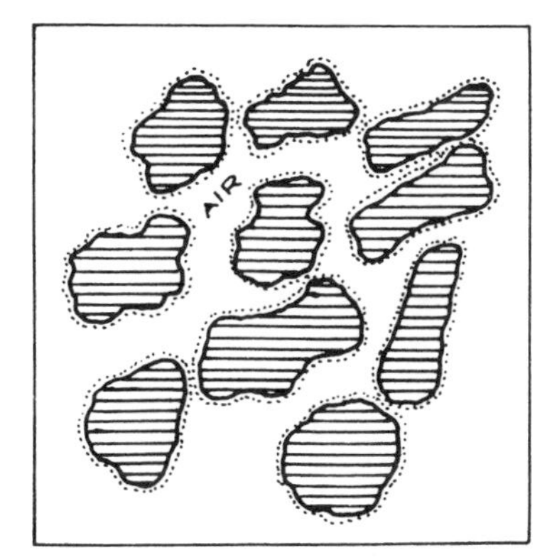

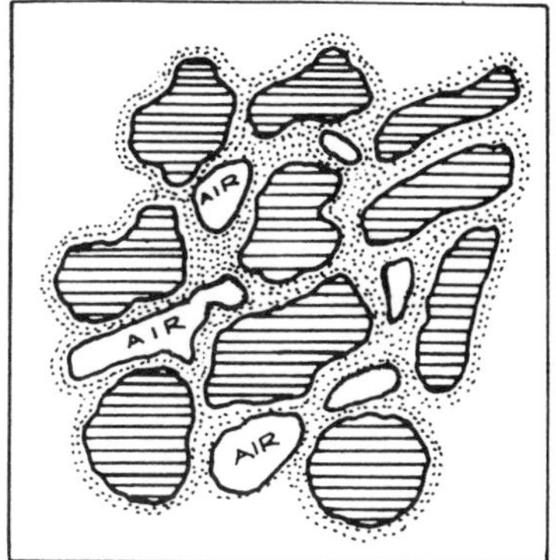

Figure 4.2: The relationship between the tension exerted on soil water by the soil particles and the moisture content of a sand and a clay soil.

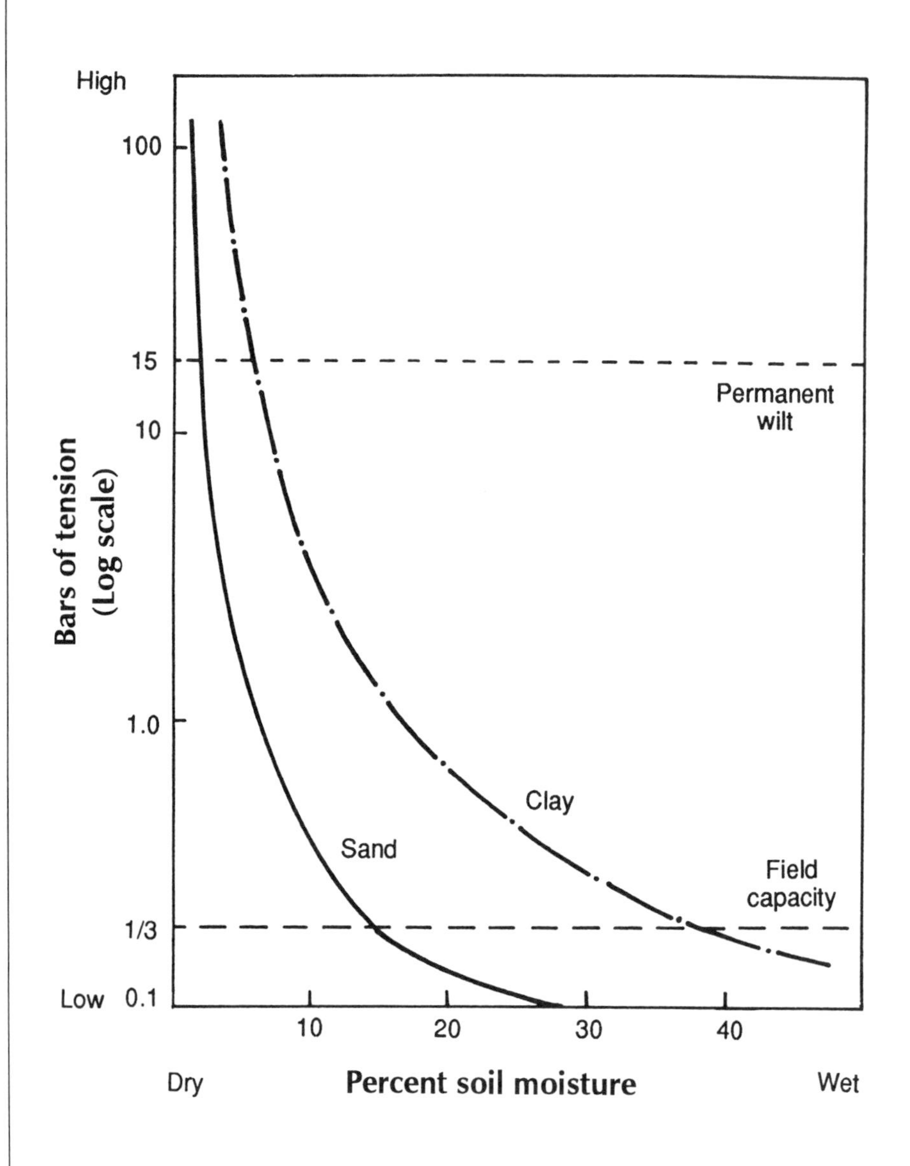

There are three points on the moisture retention curve which are related to plant growth and realistic field conditions. They are the maximum water retention capacity, field capacity and the permanent wilt point.

The maximum water retention capacity is the moisture level at which all soil pores are filled with water. Essentially the soil is saturated and contains little air. Some of the water is held with so little energy that the water will flow out of the soil due to the pull of gravity. This water is often referred to as gravitational water or drainage water and will flow out of a well-drained soil within 48 hours. Gravitational water is of only temporary value to the grass; in fact it may be argued that it is harmful water as it is excluding air from the pores. The depth in the soil profile or parent material at which the soil is saturated is known as the water table. It may be a permanent, temporary or perched water table varying in depth from a few cm to hundreds of meters.

Field capacity is the moisture content of the soil when all downward movement of water due to the pull of gravity has ceased. The water retained is often called capillary water. At this moisture content only the micro pores are filled with water and the macro pores are filled with air. It is the ideal moisture content of the soil for plant growth. The grass must exert a minimum amount of energy to absorb water from a soil at field capacity. This moisture content will exist in a soil after the gravitational water has flowed out of the macro pores. Evapotranspiration, however, causes the moisture content to continually decreases from this point until an irrigation or rain occurs.

The permanent wilt point, as the name suggests, is the moisture content at which the grass permanently wilts and will not recover if the soil is re-wetted. Actually this moisture level was initially established before the use of modern techniques of soil physics, by using sunflower seedlings which do not have the recuperative ability of turf grasses. At this point all but the finest pores are filled with air. The grass can no longer exert sufficient energy to withdraw water from the soil; so it wilts.

These three special points on the moisture retention curve are called soil moisture constants because they are reproducible values which can be determined in the lab for any soil sample. Each soil sample, however, will have its own specific curve, thus the value for the three constants will differ between soil samples.

The three moisture constants are often referred to by other terms related to the energy required to extract the water. The common term in use today is bars of tension on the water. One bar is the tension required to support a column of water 1000 cm in height. The higher the bar reading the drier the soil. Thus the maximum water retention capacity, having no tension, has a bar reading of zero (0). Field capacity has a bar reading of one-third (1/3) and the permanent wilt point has a bar reading of fifteen (15).

The difference in moisture content between field capacity and the permanent wilt point is known as the plant available water. Water remaining in the soil at the permanent wilt point obviously is unavailable to the grass. Water in excess of field capacity is removed rapidly by gravitational flow if good drainage exists so it is of little value for plant growth. As the soil becomes drier, the energy required to overcome the tension by which the water is held in the finer pores increase. Therefore it is a good practice to irrigate when 50% of the water held between field capacity and the permanent wilt point has been consumed.

Generally it is desirable to have a soil with a high percentage of plant available water (Table 4.1). Sands always contain less plant available water than clays. It is interesting to note that silts contain more plant available water than loams although the water retained at field capacity is not greatly different. The spherical nature of silt particles, however, creates a lower water content at 15 bar tension making the difference between the values for the two moisture constants greater. Likewise, the combination of the spherical shape of silt and greater amounts of easily held water contribute to the engineering problems with silt soils.

There are other factors, however, which may require a sacrifice of some of the plant available water that a silt or clay will retain when choosing a soil mix for a root zone. Principle among them is the potential for compaction and its effect on aeration. A second factor is a correctly selected and drained sand will rapidly lose any gravitational water and will seldom become anaerobic.

Table 4.1: Some values for the moisture content of soils of different textures, at three moisture constants and the amount of plant available water.

	Water Content at the Moisture Constants of			
Texture	**Maximum Retention Capacity**	**Field Capacity**	**Permanent Wilt**	**Plant Available**
		(% by weight)		
Dune Sand	32.4	6.2	2.2	4.0
Loam	46.8	28.0	14.6	13.4
Silt	47.2	30.8	9.7	21.1
Clay	58.4	40.2	29.2	11.0

CHAPTER 5

MOVEMENT OF WATER IN SOIL

Water in the soil is always moving — upward, downward and sideways — as a liquid or as a vapour — from points where it is wet to points where it is dry.

In the previous chapter an explanation was given of the physical principles by which water is held in the soil. Water, however, does not remain stationary in the soil, but is continually moving. Water always moves from places where it is wet to places where it is dry. An analogy is the end of a steel bar in a fire. Heat moves along the bar from the end in the fire to the opposite end; the end in the fire is the hottest (wettest) while the opposite end is the coldest (driest).

In soil, water primarily moves downward due to the pull or forces of gravity and is called gravitational flow. Nevertheless, at the same time water may be migrating sideways, or even upward, due to the capillary forces generated by the occurrence of the small micro pores in the soil. Figure 5.1 illustrates the various relationships between the direction and type of water flow and the moisture content of the soil immediately after rain or irrigation and after five days of drying.

Capillary Flow

While it is easy to understand that water will move down due to gravity the concept of capillary flow is less obvious. As the flow by capillary forces is through the micro pores, it is often referred to as unsaturated flow, or movement at moisture contents of field capacity or less when the soil is not saturated.

A simple illustration of capillary movement is to fill a glass to the brim with water and place a dry sponge over one half of the glass. The water in contact with the sponge will be immediately move upward into the sponge. If water is slowly added to the glass to maintain contact between the sponge and the water, it will soon be noticed that the

Figure 5.1: The direction and type of water movement in a soil profile under turf one hour and five days after irrigation or rain. The approximate tension on the water at different depths is given on the right side of the diagram.

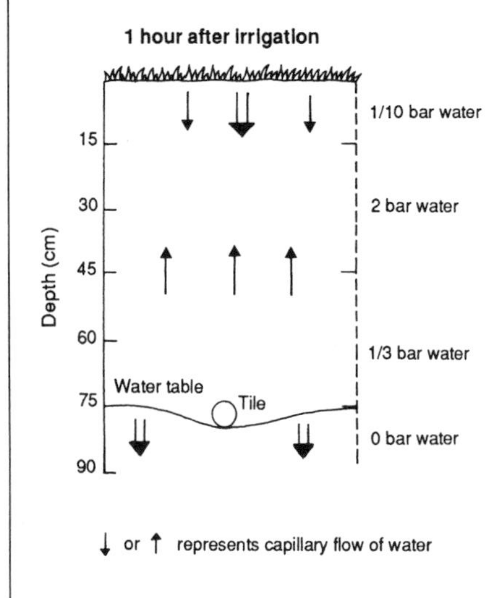

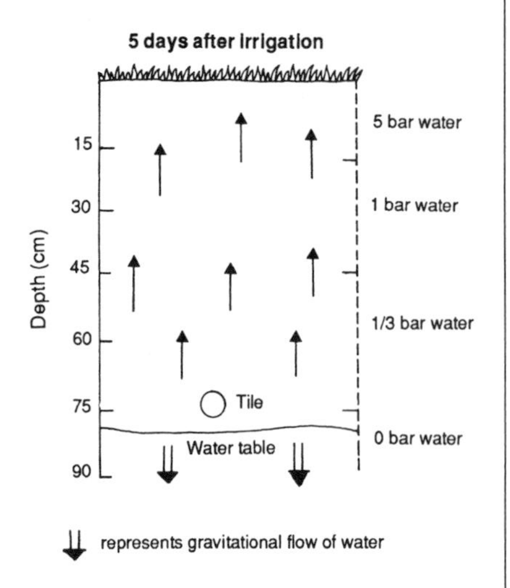

sponge is being wetted sideways from the edge of the glass as well as upward. The water is moving from an area of high concentration (in the glass) to an area of low concentration (in the dry sponge, both above and to one side of the edge of the glass). Capillary movement of water also acts downward to increase the rate of flow in the downward direction due to gravity.

Capillary movement of water is of great importance in supplying grass roots with water because it allows water to be replenished at the surface of a root as the zone within a millimetre or two adjacent to the root dries out due to the absorption of water by the grass.

The amount of water that will move to the root by this process and the rate at which it moves is dependent on the size, number and continuity of the micro pores. Large numbers of relatively small micro pores are to be found in clay soils, therefore, capillary movement is of greatest significance in fine textured soils.

The smaller the micro pores, the further the water can move by capillary forces. On the other hand, the slower it will move. In a sand-based rooting zone water can move relatively rapidly over a short distance to a root surface but the distance over which the water will travel will be measured in centimetres regardless of the time allowed. In a clay soil the water may move several metres, however, it will take weeks for this to occur.

The principle of capillary flow is employed in the design of sand-based sports fields. In the design a rooting zone 30 cm of sand is placed over gravel which creates a temporary, perched water table or zone of saturation of a few centimetres depth at the base of the sand. Water may move upward from this saturated zone to replenish the water surrounding the roots near the surface at a sufficient rate and quantity to be of importance in the growth of the turf.

Under normal soil conditions the movement of water from a water table by capillary flow at a rate to be significant in growing grass is limited to less than 30 cm. Furthermore, because the relationship between soil air and water, it is preferable in sports fields constructed on natural soil materials to not to have a water table within 60 cm of the surface. Nevertheless water in the upper 30 cm may contribute to the water supply of turf even though the root system is concentrated in the upper 15 cm.

Gravitational Flow

Flow of water by gravity is important in the rapid removal of excess water and the return of air to the system. Gravitational flow, often referred to as saturated hydraulic conductivity, occurs in the macro pores of the soil and only occurs when the moisture content of the soil rises above field capacity.

When gravitational flow is restricted, it is necessary to install artificial drainage systems. Water enters the drain line by gravitational flow. Therefore at the surface of the drain there must be a thin perched water table before water can flow into the drain system. Water cannot enter the drain by capillary flow, thus no plant available water is lost.

The determination of the saturated hydraulic conductivity, a simple laboratory procedure, is an essential measurement necessary for the design of a drainage systems and the selection of sand for sand rooting

Figure 5.2: The depth of the water table is controlled by the depth and spacing of the subsurface drain tube.

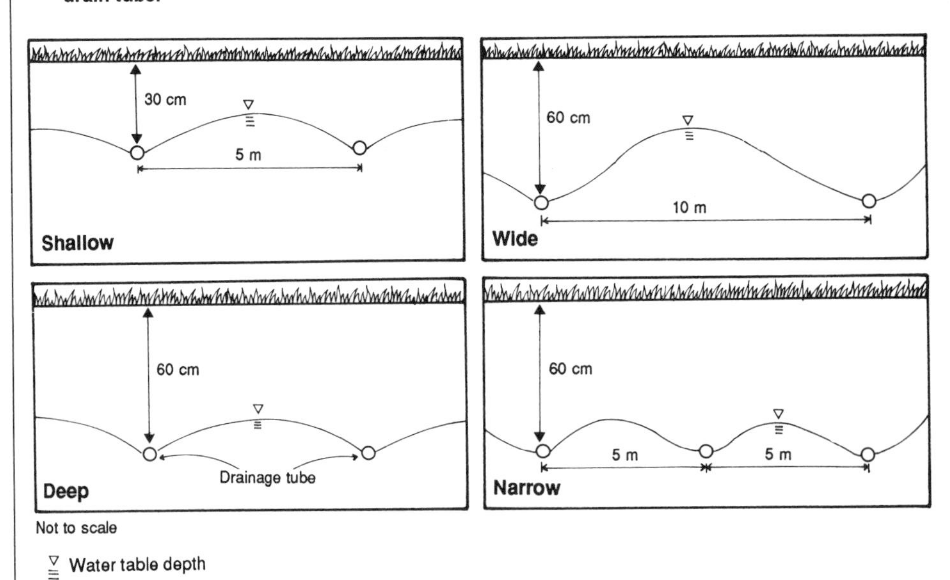

zones. The rate at which gravitational water moves through the soil is used in selecting the spacing of drain lines. The lower the saturated conductivity the closer the drain lines must be placed. Sands for root zones should have a saturated conductivity which will empty the macro pores of excess water within a few hours of heavy rain. Table 5.1 records a classification of hydraulic conductivities. Rates of seven to 10 cm/hr are acceptable for sand root zones. In natural soils rates of less than five cm/hr require very close spacing of less than five metres between drains. Figure 5.2 illustrates the influence the depth and spacing of the drain has on the water table, that point where the soil is saturated with water.

Infiltration Rate

An important measurement of soil water movement is the rate at which water enters the soil surface - the infiltration rate. The infiltration rate is an indication of the potential for erosion or water runoff, an event which seldom occurs with a turf covered surface. Under turf conditions localized ponding may occur after heavy rains, however, if the infiltration rate is low. Furthermore where the infiltration rate is low the rate at which irrigation water may be applied will be restricted. If the irrigation rate exceeds the infiltration rate runoff must occur.

Table 5.1: The saturated hydraulic conductivity classification of soil.

Drainage Class	Rate
	(cm/hr)
Extremely rapid	>50
Very rapid	50 - 15
Moderately rapid	15 - 5
Moderate	5 - 1. 5
Moderately slow	1.5 - 0.5
Slow	0.5 - 0.15
Very slow	0.15 - 0.05
Extremely slow	>0.05

Generally the infiltration rate of soils growing turf is related to the clay content, the degree of compaction and the occurrence of thatch. Soils high in clay have a lower infiltration rate than sands due to the lower percentage of macro pores. Similarly compaction, which tends to reduce the macro porosity more than the micro porosity, restricts the infiltration rate. A condition known as localized dry spots may occur where there is thatch build up, particularly if the thatch is allowed to become air dry. Due to the resistance to rewetting, the water tends to run to areas where the thatch is thinner or has not dried to the same degree, causing uneven wetting of the soil.

An infiltration rate slightly greater than the expected intensity of storm rains is desired. Under Ontario conditions the storm rain intensity is seldom greater than 75 mm per hour. Sand-based systems which have properly selected sands will have an infiltration rate that will meet this standard. To select sands which greatly exceed this requirement will mean the amount of plant available water which can be stored will be reduced.

Textural Barrier

Playing field construction using an imported material of significantly different texture from the underlying material, may create a textural discontinuity or textural barrier, and result in a perched water table. A perched water table is defined as a temporary zone of saturation (Fig. 5.3).

Textural barriers occur in turf under two widely different conditions. The first condition is found where a fine sand material is placed over small stone (Fig. 5.3 A). Due to the marked difference in pore size between the sand and the stone, water will not move from the sand into the stone layer until a zone of saturation builds up at the base of the finer sand material. The water must be at zero tension, which is saturation, before it will drip into the stone layer.

The second condition is where a course material, such as sand, is placed over clay (Fig. 5.3 B). The percolation rate in the clay may be 1000 times or more slower than in the sand, resulting in a temporary saturated zone of a few centimetres at the surface of the clay layer. Eventually as the clay dries the sand will, in reality, dry faster than if the subgrade were sand due to the increase suction placed on the sand layer from the fine micro pores in the underlying clay.

Figure 5.3 : A perched water table or zone of saturation due to a discontinuity in particle size of soil material.

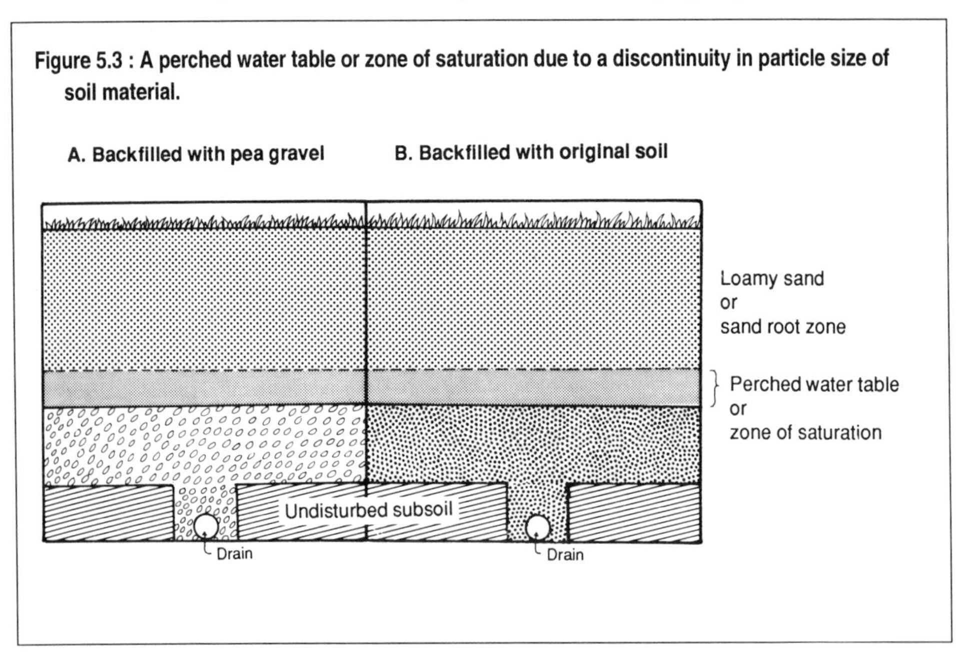

The first condition for a textural barrier is an advantage in sand-based sports field construction because it provides a reservoir of water which may move upward to the active root growth area by capillary flow. By using the perched water table principle greater water use efficiency is achieved and the frequency of irrigation is reduced.

It is interesting to note that the saturated zone at the surface of a drain tube is the result pore size discontinuity. Placing stone around the tile only moves the perched water table effect back to the interface between the stone and the soil material.

Decreasing the depth of the sand root zone to less than the recommended 30 cm has two adverse effects. It reduces the storage potential for water and it brings the saturated or anaerobic zone closer to the surface. A micro perched water table condition may also occur due to layering from topdressing or poor mixing of root zone materials. This phenomenon is the prime cause of black layer formation in sand root zones.

CHAPTER 6

EFFICIENT IRRIGATION SCHEDULING

Water is money. Use it wisely. Excessive use is damaging to the environment. Insufficient use is damaging to the grass.

There are many reasons why water is essential for turf growth — for the formation of sugar during photosynthesis, for the dissolution and absorption of plant nutrients from the soil, for the moderation of leaf temperature through transpiration or syringing, and others. Likewise there are many reasons why excessive water is detrimental to turf growth such as lack of aeration resulting in reduced root growth and eventually reduced top growth, greater susceptibility to disease, increased compaction, and increased leaching of plant nutrients, to cite a few.

Water is supplied through rainfall or irrigation. Rainfall cannot be controlled, but it is essential that the turf manager has a system whereby irrigation, which can be controlled, is scheduled to supplement rainfall. Modern automated irrigation systems greatly reduce the labour involved in irrigation, however, one or more of the disadvantages associated with excess water may easily result from "set the clock and forget it" automated systems. What is needed is a system whereby the turf manager may "set the clock" but at the same time change the settings to accommodate rainfall and changing weather conditions.

Water is lost from the system by evapotranspiration — the combination of transpiration from the leaf and evaporation from the soil surface. Under turf conditions the former is the predominate source of water loss. Water may also be lost by drainage if rainfall or irrigation exceeds the water storage capacity of the soil.

Measuring Soil Moisture

The most precise method of measuring soil moisture is to dry a soil sample at 105 C for 48 hours, and by weighing before and after determine the moisture percentage.

The installation of moisture sensing devices in the soil has been used to predict water requirements. The moisture block, which provides an electrical resistance reading, is most sensitive in relatively dry soils, but is subject to significant salt effects. Another moisture sensing device is known as a tensiometer which is sensitive at soil moisture level desirable for turf. Unfortunately the tensiometer has installation characteristics which interfere with other turf maintenance operations. It also requires considerable maintenance to give reliable data and must be removed every fall and reinstalled below the surface in the spring.

A recently developed procedure called TDR (Time Domain Refractrometry) allows measurement of soil moisture by inserting two wire probes into the soil. The original procedure provided reliable, non-destructive measurements of volumetric soil moisture. The procedure, however, required relatively expensive instrumentation and computer manipulation of the instrument readings. A portable, direct reading, and less expensive TDR probe is now available that provides excellent volumetric soil moisture measurements.

Measurement of Water Inputs

The water gained as rainfall is easily measured by the placement of a plastic rain gauge in a suitable open area near the sports field or at several locations throughout a golf course.

While irrigation equipment suppliers provide output volumes for their sprinkler heads it is a good policy to run an independent calibration of the system. The application rate may vary from that suggested in the manual due to pressure changes, wind patterns, nozzle wear, to name a few. A calibration can be obtained by removing the tops from ten juice cans and randomly placing them on the field. Water is collected for a 30-minute irrigation period. Assuming a standard 1360 ml juice can has a surface area of 86.6 cm, the total collection of water in the ten cans, measured as grams or millilitres, is divided by 866 to give the mm of added water in 30 minutes. Division of the mm of added water by the number of minutes of irrigation provides an irrigation rate of mm of water per minute.

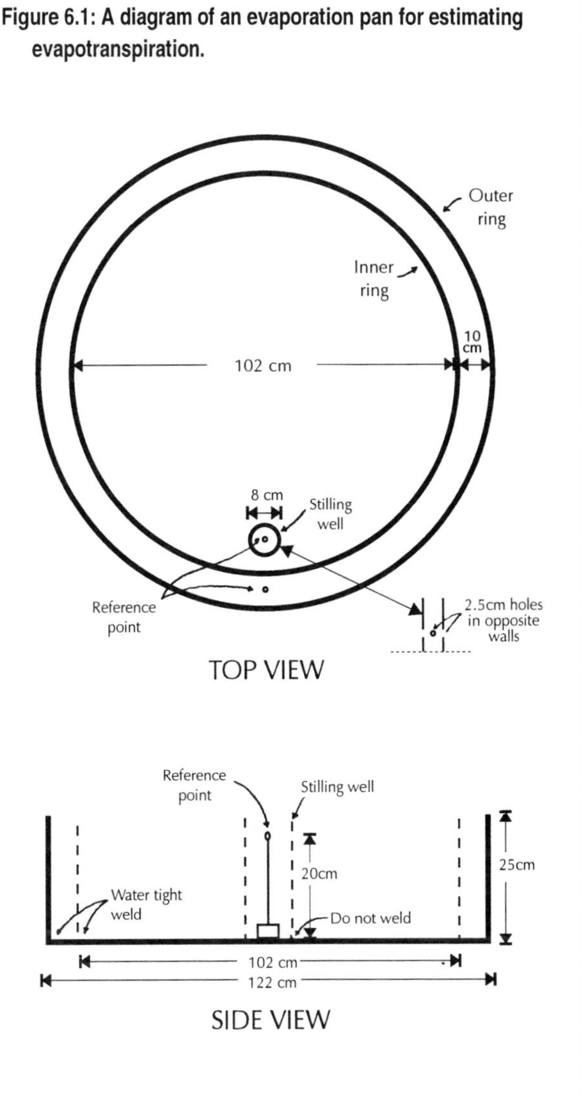

Figure 6.1: A diagram of an evaporation pan for estimating evapotranspiration.

Measurement of Evapotranspiration (ET)

Water loss by ET is not easy to measure but may be estimated by evaporation from a pan of water or from meteorological measurements. The evaporation pan procedure is more accurate but requires some expenditure in equipment and time to make the measurements and keep records.

The evaporation pan is a circular pan constructed from 2.4 mm thick, mild steel and measuring 122 cm in diameter and 25 cm deep (Fig. 6.1). Ten cm inside the outer ring a second ring is welded to the base to provide a watertight seal. An 8-cm diameter by 25-cm deep stilling well stands near the edge of the inner compartment. A sharp pointed brass rod reference point, anchored in a lead base block and adjusted to a total length of 20 cm is placed in the centre of the stilling well. A similar pointed brass rod is placed between the inner and outer rings. The evaporation pan is placed on a slatted wooden platform 10 cm above ground level in a non-shaded area, open to the free flow of the wind. A few crystals of copper sulphate (bluestone) are added to prevent algae growth.

Water is added to the inner and outer compartments to bring the water up to the level where the point of the brass rod just breaks the water surface. Each morning the weight of water (g) or volume of water (ml) required to bring the water level back to that point in the inner compartment is measured. If rain during the previous 24 hours has exceeded the amount of ET, the amount of water which must be removed to return the water to the point is recorded. To obtain the ET value it is necessary to subtract the amount of water which was removed from the amount of rainfall, both in mm. When the rainfall is less than ET, the amount of rainfall is added to the mm of water used to re level the inner tank to give the total ET for the previous day. The amount of water removed or added in mm is obtained by dividing the weight (g), or volume (ml), of water removed or added by 817 which is 1/10 the surface area of the inner compartment (Table 6.1).

Table 6.1: How to calculate pan evaporation.

Weather Situation	Formula for Pan Evaporation in mm
1. No. rain. Added "A" g or ml of water to pan to get correct level	A/817
2. Small rain of "R" mm. Added "A" g or ml of water to pan to get correct level	R + A/817
3. Big rain of "R" mm. Took "E" g or ml of water from pan to get correct level	R - E/817

It is known that evaporation from the water surface in the pan is greater than from grass leaves and that it changes with the time of the season, hence a correction factor must be applied to give an estimate of the actual grass ET. Research indicates the factor changes with time of season from 0.45 to 0.75 (Table 6.2).

Table 6.2: Correction factors for adjusting pan evaporation to grass ET.

Month	Correction Factor*
April	0.45
May	0.55
June	0.65
July	0.75
August	0.75
September	0.55
October	0.45

* Pan Evaporation x Correction Factor = Grass ET.

Table 6.3: Estimators for pan evaporation based on observed weather conditions.

One p.m. Weather Observations for				Estimated Pan
Sunshine	Temperature	Humidity*	Wind**	Evaporation (mm)
Full	Greater than 23C	Low	High	8.0
Full	Greater than 23C	Low	Low	7.5
Full	Greater than 23C	High	High	7.0
Full	Greater than 23C	High	Low	6.5
Full	Less than 23C	Low	High	6.5
Full	Less than 23C	Low	Low	6.0
Full	Less than 23C	High	High	5.5
Full	Less than 23C	High	Low	5.0
Cloudy	Greater than 23C	Low	High	5.0
Cloudy	Greater than 23C	Low	Low	4.5
Cloudy	Greater than 23C	High	High	4.0
Cloudy	Greater than 23C	High	Low	3.5
Cloudy	Less than 23C	Low	High	3.5
Cloudy	Less than 23C	Low	Low	3.0
Cloudy	Less than 23C	High	High	2.5
Cloudy	Less than 23C	High	Low	2.0

*Low = clear sky, unlimited visibility; High = smog, haze, fog.

** Low = leaves and small branches moving; High = tree tops moving

An alternative, less accurate, but adequate for irrigation purposes, method for estimating grass ET is to record daytime weather conditions such as sunshine, temperature, wind velocity and humidity (Table 6.3). Visual estimates of the four factors along with the correction factors found in Table 6.2 can be used to allow the calculation of an estimate of pan evaporation (Table 6.3). Analysis of the relative importance of the four variables has shown that sunshine and temperature have the greatest effect on ET.

Water Storage Capacity

To develop an irrigation scheduling system it is necessary to estimate the amount of plant available water (see Chapter 4) retained in the rooting zone of the turf. The estimate may be known for sand rooting systems where the water characteristics of the sand were determined prior to construction. Alternatively the volume of plant available water may be measured in core samples submitted to a laboratory for field capacity and permanent wilt point determinations.

It is generally accepted that irrigation should occur when 50% of the plant available water has been lost through ET. At this time sufficient water should be added to raise the water content of the rooting zone back to, or slightly above, field capacity. Any water in addition to this amount will be wasted through drainage loss.

For fields not based on U.S.G.A. specifications it is necessary to estimate, preferably by direct observation, the depth of rooting. Turf with a high proportion of annual bluegrass may have an effective rooting depth of 5 cm whereas tall fescue may be rooting to 30 cm. Compacted soils with have proportionally less effective rooting depth.

The Water Budget

A water budget may be set up to estimate of the volume of plant available water in the rooting zone which is analogous to maintaining a bank account balance. A value, equivalent to 50% of the plant available water, serves as the water budget base line which must not be exceeded if water stress to the turf is to be avoided (minimum bank balance). Water removed from the rooting zone by grass ET (cheques written) is recorded daily and subtracted from the estimate of plant available water (Table 6.4). When rainfall occurs it is added to the plant available water balance (pay cheque deposited). When rain has not occurred by the time the balance approaches the water budget base line sufficient irrigation must be applied to return the budget to the plant available water level (lottery winnings). When rainfall or rainfall plus irrigation occurs which supply more water than necessary to raise the budget above the plant available water level the difference will be lost as drainage water (income tax paid) and the budget will remain at the plant available water level. A hypothetical example of a water budget for a sports field having a storage capacity of 40 mm of water and a water budget base line of 20 mm is provided in Table 6.4.

Table 6.4: A hypothetical water budget record sheet for sand rooting zone having a water storage of 40 mm of plant available water in the rooting zone at the time records start.

	Water Input*		Water Output*		
Date	Rainfall	Irrigation	Evaporation	Drainage	Balance
		((mm)			
Aug. 7	0	0	-6.0	0	34.0
Aug. 8	+3.0	0	-2.6	0	34.4
Aug. 9	0	0	-6.0	0	28.4
Aug. 10	0	0	-5.25	0	23.15
Aug. 11	0	+15.0	-4.2	0	33.95
Aug. 12	+18.0	0	-3.0	8.95	40.00
Aug. 13	0	0	-4.0	0	36.0
Aug. 14	0	0	-2.8	0	33.2

*All measurements made at 9:00 a.m.

Pan evaporation was used to develop a water budget system of irrigation scheduling for an installation of U.S.G.A. micro greens at the Cambridge Research Station, in 1983. A plot of the daily records of pan evaporation, rainfall, irrigation and drainage loss for the period of June 30 to August 1 were used to schedule irrigation (Fig. 6.2). The system had an estimated storage capacity of 50 mm of plant available water in a 30-cm depth, hence at 50% use of plant available water irrigation should occur when 25 mm of water has been consumed by plant growth. On June 30 the budget indicated a positive value of +0.7 mm, a value which fell to -23 mm by July 8 when it approached the water budget base line which signalled the need for irrigation.

Note that irrigation was not required every day, even on the sand rooting zone. The maximum ET was about 8 mm, thus a storage of 25

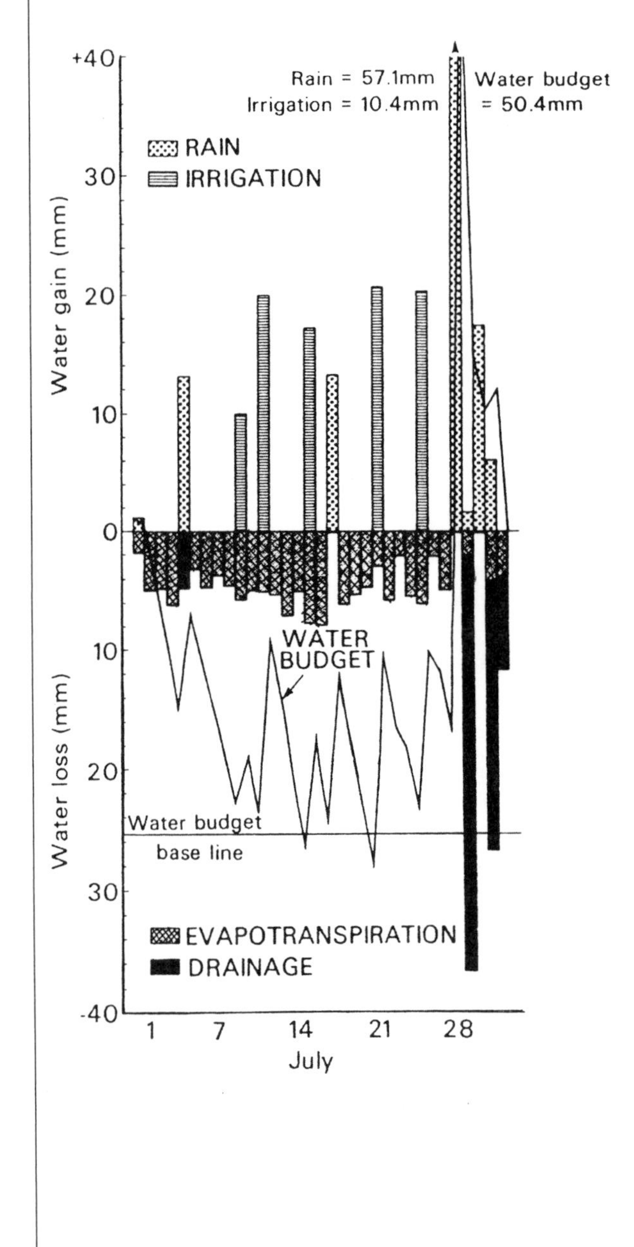

Figure 6.2: The water input through rain and irrigation and loss through evapotranspiration and drainage during July, 1983, on the micro greens at the Cambridge Research Station.

mm of water would provide sufficient water for a minimum of three days without irrigation.

During the period irrigation was used six times and rain occurred six times, with a particularly heavy, 57.4 mm rain on July 28 and lesser amounts on the three subsequent days. The July 28 rain was preceded by 10.4 mm of irrigation which had been called for by the water budget. As a result a drainage loss of 69 mm occurred over the following days as the rainfall continued. Such occurrences cannot always be avoided as it is impossible to predict the intensity and duration of summer storms.

More recent research has shown that the observed weather observations can serve as a reliable substitute for pan evaporation measurements.

Laboratory analysis of the root zone material for a U.S.G.A. designed green at the Guelph Turfgrass Institute indicated the 30-cm depth had an available water storage 30 mm, hence irrigation should occur after 15 mm of water loss by evapotranspiration. Weather observations observed during the July 12 to 25 period (Table 6.5) served as the basis for the water budget used to schedule the irrigation (Table 6.6). Water stress was not observed at any time during this period.

Figure 6.3: The soil moisture profile for a sand root zone green at the Guelph Turfgrass Institute immediately before and two hours after irrigation. The 20-mbar line represents the apparent field capacity for a sand and the 40-mbar line represents the point where moisture stress may occur on the green.

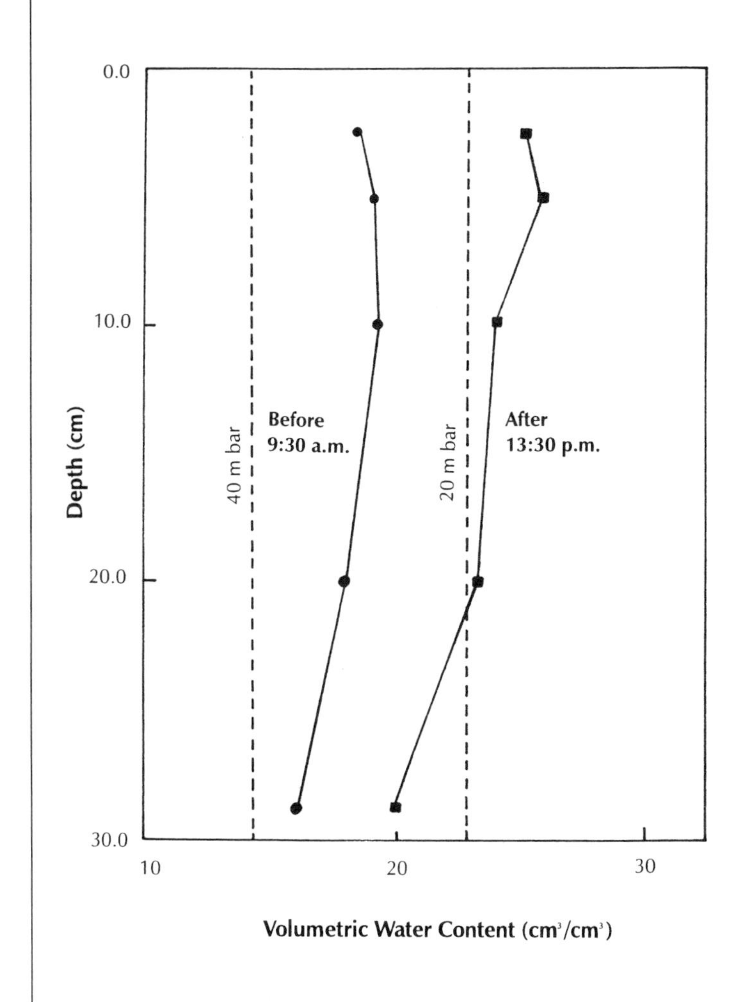

Table 6.5 Weather observations for July 12 to July 25 at the Guelph Turfgrass Institute.

Date	Sun	Temp.	Humidity	Wind	E.T.	Adj. E.T.
July 12	Full	27	Low	Low	7.5	5.0
13	Full	30	High	Low	6.5	4.9
14	Full	32	High	Low	6.5	4.9
15	Full	30	High	Low	6.5	4.9
16	Full	29	Low	Low	7.5	5.6
17	Full	31	High	High	7.0	5.2
18	Full	28	Low	Low	7.5	5.6
19	Full	24	Low	Low	7.5	5.6
20	Full	22	Low	Low	6.0	4.5
21	Cloud	21	Low	Low	3.0	2.2
22	Full	23	Low	Low	3.0	2.2
23	Full	25	Low	Low	7.5	5.5
24	Cloud	21	High	Low	2.0	1.5
25	Cloud	23	Low	Low	3.0	2.2

Table 6.6: The water budget for a sand root zone at the Guelph Turfgrass Institute based on weather observations (Table 6.5) for the July 11 to July 25 and which resulted in the water profile illustrated in Figure 6.3.

Date	Rain	Irrigation	E.T.	Drainage	Balance
		(mm)			
11					15.0*
12	0	0	5.6	0	9.4
13	0	0	4.9	0	4.5
14	0	18	4.9	2.6	15.0
15	16.2	0	4.9	11.3	15.0
16	0	0	5.6	0	9.4
17	0	0	5.2	0	4.2
18	0	15	5.6	0	13.6
19	0	0	5.6	0	8.0
20	0	0	4.5	0	3.5
21	13.0	0	2.2	0	14.3
22	0	0	2.2	0	8.7
23	0	0	5.6	0	3.1
24	0	0	1.5	0	1.6
25	0	19	2.2	2.2	15.0

* One-half of the storage capacity of the root zone.

Water content of the root zone was measured by a TDR system immediately prior to irrigation and two hours after irrigation (Fig. 6.3). Prior to irrigation on July 25 the TDR system indicated the moisture content had fallen to half way between filed capacity (20-mbar line) and the moisture stress level (40-mbar) and the water budget showed 1.6 mm of water remaining before the 50% level was reached. Irrigation of 19 mm was applied and the water budget was recharged, in fact there was a potential for a drainage loss of 2.2 mm.

It is interesting to note the near vertical orientation of the line representing the change in moisture content with depth. This near vertical line indicates the bentgrass was uniformly withdrawing water throughout the 30-cm profile, an indication of the rapid capillary rise of water from depth to the mass of roots in the upper 15 cm of the root zone.

Water conservation will become an important issue for turf managers in the future. The water budget system has shown a minimum saving of 25% over automated timing systems. Saving water can also contribute to saving fertilizer, particularly nitrogen, and pesticides, thus improving the environmental impact of sports turf, a win-win procedure.

CHAPTER 7

SOIL COMPACTION

A major problem facing every manager of intensively used grass is compaction. While surface wear from intensive use will visibly remove above ground vegetation, simultaneously a non-visible problem may be occurring below the surface in the form of compaction.

The sub grade of a highway is compacted to a high density to restrict water movement and eliminate air spaces. A similar situation often exists following sports field construction and is the antithesis of grass root growth.

The Cause and Effect of Compaction

The combination of wear and compaction creates a twofold restriction on root development of the grass plant. Removal of top growth reduces photosynthesis. Thus, there is a decline in the food required for root growth. Compaction reduces the porosity of the soil, restricting normal exchange of oxygen and carbon dioxide and other potentially toxic gases. Under very compacted conditions root elongation may also be impeded. The total effect on root growth is thus much greater than would be expected through removal of top growth only.

Compaction occurs when the soil particles moved into closer fitting arrangements. Water is the lubricant which facilitates the movement. Thus play under wet conditions when the soil is near saturation is more likely to lead to compaction than when the soil is dry. Drainage to remove excess water rapidly from the root zone is the one step which may be taken to assist in long term correction of a compaction problem.

The clay content of the soil is another very important factor in compaction. While sand and silt particles may be spherical or angular in shape, clay particles tend to be flat; hence they are often referred to as clay plates. These clay plates easily slide over each other and tend to become layered under pressure at high moisture contents. The porosity decreases as the layered arrangement becomes more prevalent. In addition the much smaller clay particles tend to slide into the pores between the larger sand and silt particles, intensifying the reduction in porosity.

If you have ever observed a road being constructed, you would have seen the water truck spraying on water, followed by the various types of rollers. The contractor is attempting to maximize compaction by providing heavy traffic at a high soil moisture content. But a compacted roadbed is obviously not the media for growing grass.

Thus compaction results from traffic, whether it comes from the player's foot or from the machines used in construction or maintenance. Many sport fields, fairways and greens are seriously compacted at the end of the construction process; and also to a significant depth. The size of the equipment used in reshaping the subgrade and moving the root zone into place, combined with the repetitive trips by the motor grader to establish the finished grade, invariably results in a compacted system before the turf is ever seeded or sodded.

Often the contractor is under time restraints. Thus some, or all of the work may be conducted with these large machines under excessively wet conditions. The primary business of most earth moving contractors is in road construction; they just following their normal practices when they get a relatively small contract for a playing field or golf course.

It is important that the turf manager realizes that compaction may exist before the field is sodded or seeded and he should endeavour to correct the problem before establishing the grass. Deep tillage with heavy duty aerifiers or even the use of a farm-type chisel plough, operated in several directions, will assist in reducing the initial compaction. For maximum effect the procedure is to do the remedial aerification or tillage when the soil is somewhat less than field capacity; that is - *dry*.

Compaction is the cumulative effect of frequency and intensity of pressure applied to the soil surface. Pressure is the weight of the pedestrian or vehicle divide by the surface area actually in contact with the soil. The area of contact should be as large as possible; thus the use of turf tires or flotation tires on turf maintenance equipment.

James Beard provides some interesting numbers in his book, Turfgrass, Science & Culture, on the effect of the athletes' footwear on the pressure applied to the soil surface. He compared a 100-kilogram person wearing football shoes versus wearing regular street shoes. A street shoe contains approximately 206 cm^2 of effective surface area. In walking the 100-kg person would exert a pressure of 450 g/cm^2. In contrast, a football shoe has seven, 0.9 cm diameter cleats, providing an effective surface area of 8.4 cm^2 in contact with the soil. Thus, the static pressure exerted by the 100-kg person increases to 8095 g/cm^2 under his running foot.

Compaction due to the athlete or to turf maintenance equipment is generally confined to the upper 7.5 cm. In many cases it may be a zone of 2.5 cm or less.

Correcting the Compaction Problem

The remedy for compaction of existing turf is turf cultivation, often called aerification. The principal types of cultivation for the relief of compaction are coring, slicing, and spiking.

The three cultivation machines may be divided into two distinctly different systems based on their physical operation. Coring is the practice by which hollow tines or spoons are used to extract cores of soil to a depth of five to 7.5 cm. On the other hand, slicing is a procedure in which a solid knife, mounted on a rotating drum, is sliced into the top five to 7.5 cm of soil. Spiking is a similar procedure in which a solid spike or prong is forced into the soil up to 15 cm and withdrawn. The spike may be vibrated to a degree to cause some shattering effect to the surrounding soil.

The two systems are distinctly different in operation because they involve two different principles. Coring involves the removal of an intact core of soil which is deposited on the surface or removed from the site. It results in a minimum disturbance of the surrounding soil (Fig. 7.1). Compaction is alleviated by breaking up the removed cores and matting them back into the holes, or removing the cores from the site and backfilling the holes with a suitable topdressing material. The procedure is best performed when the soil moisture is at field capacity to reduce the force required to penetrate the compacted soil and to assist in removing intact cores (Fig 7.2). The cores may be easily broken and matted or vertically mowed back into the surface following

Figure 7.1: An illustration of coring versus spiking. The length of arrows represents the relative amount of compression of displaced soil into the surrounding soil. The wavy lines indicate the zone of shattering.

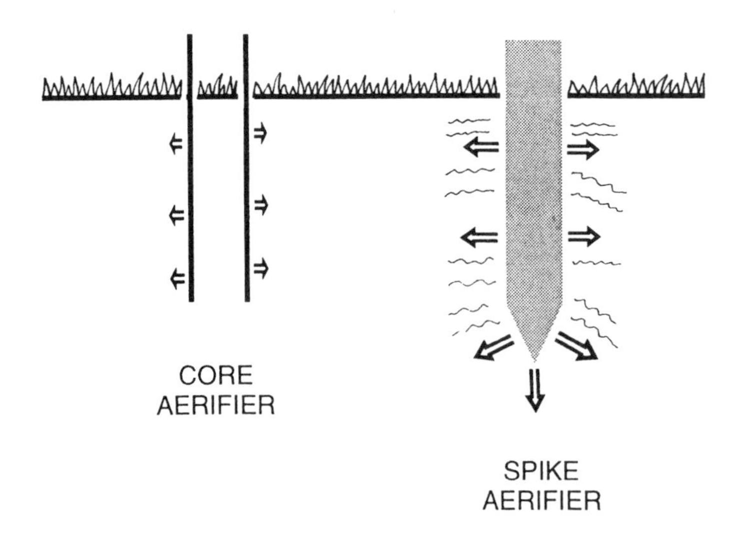

Figure 7.2: An aerifier removing and depositing cores on the surface which may serve as topdressing material.

two or three hours of drying on a sunny day. Allowing the cores of a clay soil to become completely dry may result in nearly rocklike objects which cannot be broken until the next rain or irrigation.

Slicing and spiking involves forcing a knife or prong into the soil and opening a slit or hole. The soil existing in the volume occupied by the slit or hole must be forced sideways or upward, thus increasing the density of the soil in the immediate vicinity of the slice or hole (Fig. 7.1). Relief of compaction occurs when there is a vibration effect associated with the penetration of the knife or prong which shatters the compacted zone. To maximize the vibration effect, cultivation with slicers or spikers should be done under relatively dry conditions, which in turn requires more force to permit penetration of the knife or prong.

Slicing and spiking is generally less disruptive of the turf surface and is less labour intensive than coring. They are used, therefore, as a routine operation for entire fields or fairways whereas coring may be restricted to high traffic areas where overseeding is to be done or the root zone is to be modified by the addition of a topdressing material.

Coring is a practice which should be integrated with overseeding as loose soil is provided to aid in covering of the seed and improvement of germination. At the same time it must be realized that weed seeds are also encouraged to germinate, a factor which applies to all types of turf cultivation which disturbs the dense canopy of turf. Scheduling turf cultivation to seasons when annual weed germination is not a significant factor, such as early fall, can reduce the problem.

The total removal of a compacted zone by coring will take a number of years. During a coring operation a 1.9 cm diam. core, on 5.0 cm centres, will remove 1076 cm^2 of surface area per square meter per operation. Assuming that the machine may be driven in each operation so that no recoring of the same hole occurs, it would take a minimum of nine operations to remove the compacted layer over an area of one meter.

It is generally recommended that cultivation not be performed when the turf is under heat or moisture stress. Other good management practices, such as irrigation, nitrogen fertilization and correct mowing height, which contribute to vigorous turf, should be in operation in conjunction with cultivation. Nevertheless, the need for relatively dry conditions to optimize the shattering effect of spiking should not be overlooked.

One of the principal reasons for the construction of all sand rooting zones for turf are to avoid the problems of compaction. Sands, selected according to the USGA specifications, do not compact to any significant degree beyond that which exists at the completion of construction. While the resulting porosity of all sand rooting zones may be ten percentage points less than that of a normal soil, one is assured that it will remain constant over time, as will the relationship between micro and macro porosity, even under a high level of use. The same cannot be said for fields built with clay soils where the macro porosity will be reduced by compaction during construction and while the field is in use.

CHAPTER 8

BUILDING THE SPORTS FIELD

Initial Decisions

The concepts of the science of soils have been combined with the knowledge of the physiology of plant growth to design a set of of guidelines for the construction of root zones for the optimum conditions for plant growth. Following those guidelines can lead to success; deviations from the guidelines may result in disaster.

Municipal governments, school boards and service clubs are prone to allocating money for the construction of a new sports field with minimal investigation of the requirements for the use of the facility. Often the questions which are asked by the authorities are "What type of stadium should we have?", "What should we be specifying in the tender?"

The cart is now before the horse! Among the questions which should have been asked first are: "What is the level of expectation of the field?", "What are the management requirements for maintaining the field - labour, equipment, irrigation, on going funding?" "Will there be night games?" Then the funding should be allocated.

Any funding organization contemplating the construction of a new sports field should begin their discussion with the first of the above questions. The level of funding for both construction and maintenance depends on the "level of expectation of the field", not the sport which will use the field - soccer, football, field hockey, etc. In many cases the cost and quality of the field bears no relationship to the cost and quality of the infrastructure.

The "level of expectation" of the field may be divided into three categories. The highest category - a Category I field - is the most expensive to construct and maintain. This is the field where professional or semi-professional league and tournament play will take place. An infrastructure of stands, change rooms, lights, etc., is included in the budget, and often cost more than the actual field. A further criterion for this category is that pre-game seat sales will occur, thus that cancellation of a game is not an acceptable alternative. This category calls for the construction to follow the U.S.G.A. specifications for golf greens construction. Category I fields should never be attempted without a guaranteed, uninterrupted water supply.

The middle category - a Category II field - is the most difficult to define, and also to design. It is the field where play is generally scheduled, but may be cancelled due to field or weather conditions and where limited infrastructure in the form of change rooms and stands are provided. Lights are often included. Even so, the quality of turf should be high and the construction such that heavy use may be entertained for all levels of competition.

The lowest category - a Category III field - is the local neighbourhood facility for minor league play and unscheduled play by the general public. No change rooms, stands or other facilities are available and minimum security fencing is necessary to contain the play. The quality of the turf should be such that good ground cover is maintained to insure the safety of the user.

Regardless of the "level of expectation" it must be kept in mind that good ground cover must be maintained at all times to insure the safety of the user. The use is for running sports where the play player must keep his eye on the ball and rely on the turf manager to provide him with a safe, uniform surface on which to run.

The Drainage System

The first requirement of a field in any of the three categories should be to assure that adequate surface drainage is available. While mandatory for Category I and II fields, which during construction will be graded to a defined slope or crown, Category III fields often accept the natural grade or slope of the site. Such acceptance in turn will lead to future problems where low areas pond water, increasing the potential damage to the turf. Extra funding to insure a proper surface grade prior to seeding the field will result in lower maintenance costs in the future. Due to the high saturated hydraulic conductivity of Category I fields, they may be built without a crown.

The design of all sports fields of Category I and II must begin with an adequate subsurface drainage system in addition to surface drainage.

The first step in designing the subsurface drainage system is to provide a satisfactory outlet for any drainage water. The outlet most probably will be the storm water drainage system.

Drains are 10-cm, perforated, plastic tubes spaced at least every 12 metres apart, but in impervious clay soils or sand based rooting zones they should not be more than six metres apart. Due to the low cost relative to other items in the construction of a field it is often advisable to space the lines six metres apart, or less, under all soil conditions.

Some installers prefer to use a herringbone design. The design adds nothing to the efficiency of the system and may contribute slightly to the cost. The simplest and most cost efficient system from the installer's viewpoint are lines running the length of the field: commencing at mid-field, with a falling grade, and extending at least six metres beyond the playing surface at the end of the field. An additional line outside the playing surface for the players bench area is often advisable.

Tile lines should be installed at a minimum depth of 45 cm below the finished surface grade. A mid-field depth of 45 cm will result in a depth of 60 to 90 cm at the point where the line enters the main line to the outlet. The drain lines are installed at a 0.5 to 1.0% grade (15 cm fall/30 metres of run) to insure the lines are self flushing. Remember there is a 0.10% grade in 100 meters of a 10-cm tube if it were installed perfectly level.

It is not necessary to place stone below the tile line, unless the stone is used to obtain a uniform grade on the line when the trench is opened with a backhoe. Do not lay the drain tube on loose soil as settlement will soon cause valleys where sediment will collect and plug the drain. Many installations are made with a backhoe which does not provide the grade control obtainable with the laser-controlled excavating wheel or chain used on commercial tile laying machines. The use of a laser-controlled, tile laying machine is not only more accurate, but faster, and worthy of serious consideration by the contractor. Likewise it is not necessary to enclose the drain line in geotechnic material unless the native soil is a very fine sandy loam or a silt.

The drain lines should be installed after the subgrade has been graded to the desired slope of the surface of the field. Installing the lines under wet conditions can destroy the smooth subgrade by leaving ruts thus preventing the free movement of water laterally to the drain lines in the future. Regrading of a disturbed surface may be difficult as the graded material should not be spilled onto the drain lines. Crushing of the lines can occur if heavy machinery is used over freshly laid lines, therefore care must be exercised in movement of the remaining materials into place by restricting truck movement and plank bridging over the lines.

Category I fields require a special addition to the drainage system, the placement of a 15-cm depth of stone above the tile and over the entire subgrade surface (Fig. 8.1). The selection of the size of the stone is critical because the migration of the finer materials used in the rooting zone into the stone blanket must be avoided if the drainage system is to function properly for decades into the future.

U.S.G.A. specifications call for a stone layer having 65% of the stone in the range of 0.5 cm to 1.0 cm, with not more than 10% greater than 1.25 cm, and not more than 10% below 0.25 cm. The stone layer

Fig. 8.1: A cross section of a sand-based rooting zone for turf.

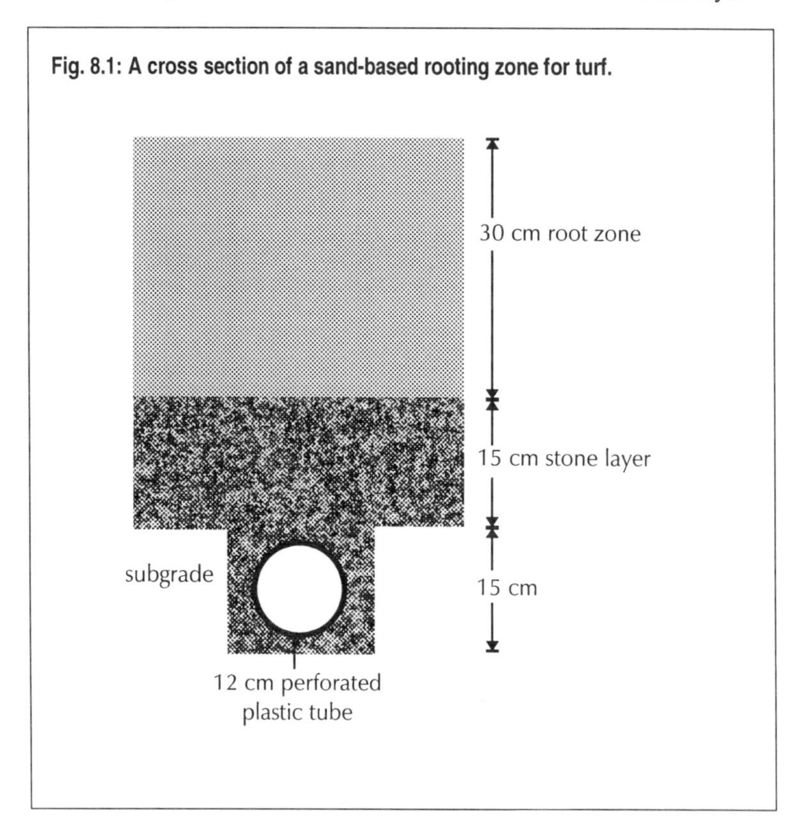

is then covered with a 7.5-cm layer of course sand (choker layer) to provide the necessary bridging over the large pores in the stone. Installation of the choker layer, however, is a slow, labour intensive operation.

An alternative, now accepted by the U.S.G.A., is the recommendation to use a smaller stone without the choker layer. For bridging of the root zone particles over the pores in the stone layer to occur the D_{15} (diam. below which 15% of the stone particles lie) of the stone must be less than or equal to five times the D_{85} (diam. below which 85% of the sand particles lie) of the root zone mix. Likewise, for adequate permeability of water to occur the D_{15} of the stone must be greater than or equal to five times the D_{15} of the root zone mix. Finally the stone should have a gradation index ($D_{90}/_{15}$) less than or equal to 2.5. It is preferable that the stone be an angular shape, suggesting well-screened, crushed aggregate. An example of the size distribution

Fig. 8.2: The envelope for the particle size distribution of the stone layer for use without a choker layer of sand.

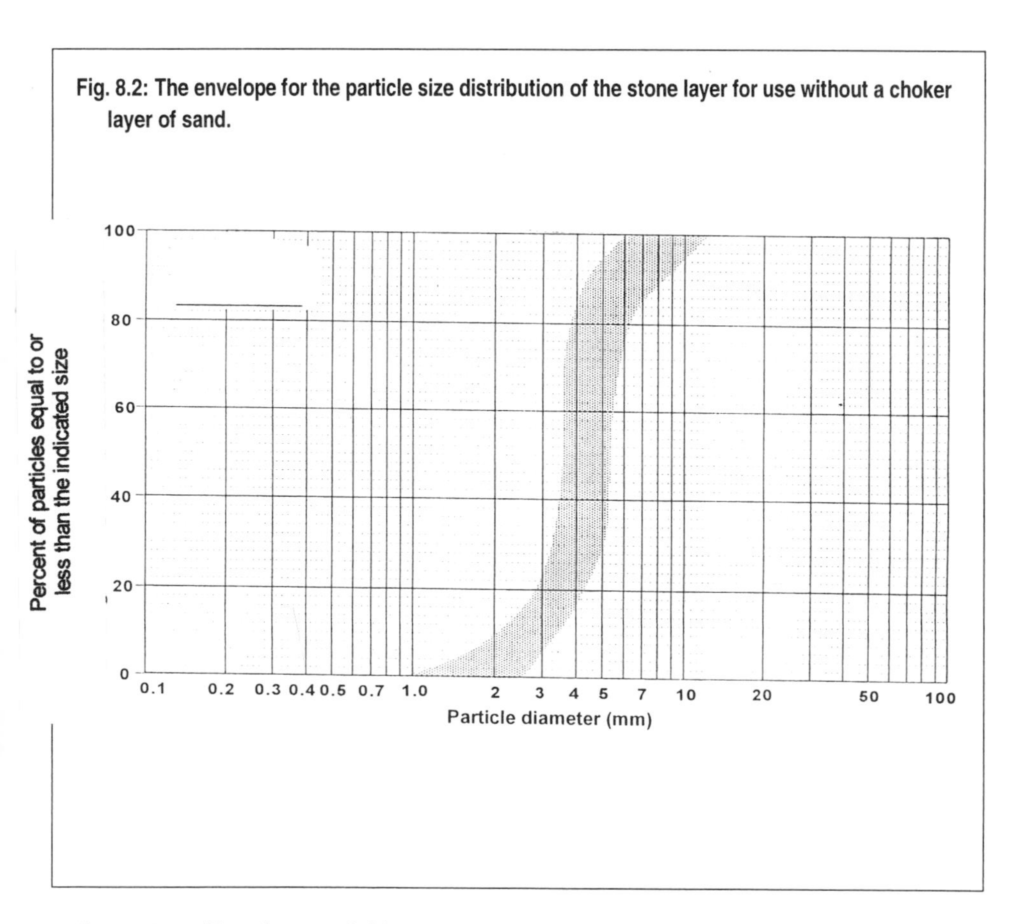

of a satisfactory material and the distribution envelope within which suitable materials will fall is provided in Figure 8.2.

The Rooting Zone

The next step in the process of construction of Category I and II fields is the selection of the rooting zone mix. Whatever material is used, the rooting zone should be a minimum of 30 cm in depth (Fig. 8.1). The same care must be exercised in placing the root zone material over the stone as was used in putting the stone in place, otherwise rutting and intermixing with the stone will occur.

Many Category II fields are constructed using the native soil for the rooting zone. Prior to approving a native soil for use it should be subjected to particle size analysis and moisture transmission analysis. The textural class of the soil should be a course sandy loam or loamy sand and should have less than a total of 10% silt plus clay. Silt loams and clays should be avoided. It should have the ability to transmit a minimum of 2.5 cm of water per hour.

The rooting zone of all Category I field should be based on the principles of U.S.G.A. greens construction. The principles involve the construction of a drain and stone blanket drainage system on which is placed a special root zone mix. The mix comprises a selected sand to which a relatively small amount of soil and/or organic material is added. It is preferred that only soil without organic amendments be used. The soil acts as an innoculant of the natural soil microbial population to an otherwise sterile sand. The resulting mixture will not be subject to future compaction and will have water transmission values which will permit play under all weather conditions while minimizing the damage to the grass.

Often an attempt is made to ameliorate an existing soil with sand to provide a root zone mix. This procedure involves a high risk of making a mix which is highly compactable and which has a low ability to transmit water.

A satisfactory mix, however, can be prepared if the sand is carefully selected to meet the requirements of a Category I field and a particle size analysis for the soil to be used is known. The number of tonnes of sand to be mixed with 100 tonnes of soil is provided by the equation

$$A = \frac{(R - B)}{(C - R)} \times 100$$

where A = the weight of sand to add to 100 tonnes of the original soil;
B = % of the original soil in the 0.125 mm to 0.50 mm size range;
C = % of 0.125 mm to O.50 mm size range in the selected sand;
R = the desired % of 0.125 mm to 0.50 mm sand in the final mixture. An R value of at least 80 is necessary to obtain reasonable water characteristics. For estimating purposes one hectare to a 10-mm depth is approximately 100 tonnes at a bulk density of 1.0.

It is essential that the mix be prepared off-site. Furthermore a preliminary mix should be checked for its saturated hydraulic conductivity. For many soils the cost of amelioration of an existing soil will approach that of a sand-based root zone.

The selection of the sand for the root zone is critical. The procedures to follow are outlined below.

Several potential suppliers of sand should be selected and asked to submit a two-kilogram sample for particle size analysis. The suppliers should be asked to supply a brick sand or topdressing sand, because these are the trade names for materials which will most probably fit the U.S.G.A. requirements. The samples should be sent to a laboratory capable of performing sieve analysis of sand and characterizing the moisture relationships of the final mix.

Suitable sands should be selected on the basis of a particle size distribution which falls within the envelope illustrated in Figure 8.3. Care should be taken to select a sand that is very low in silt and clay size particles (less than or equal to 0.05 mm) because upon the addition of the soil material the final mix must not exceed a total of 8% silt plus clay. Having two or more samples which meet these criteria the contractor is in a position to negotiate price, supply, delivery, etc., with the suppliers.

The next or concurrent step is the selection of a suitable top soil to add to the sand. The preferred soil should be a screened material containing no stones or other debris, weed free, herbicide free, have a high organic matter content and have a sandy loam texture. Samples from potential sources should be subjected to particle size analysis for percent sand, silt and clay by hydrometer analysis, percent organic matter and percent total carbonates. Samples containing less than two

Fig. 8.3: The envelope of the particle size distribution of the sand for the rooting zone mix.

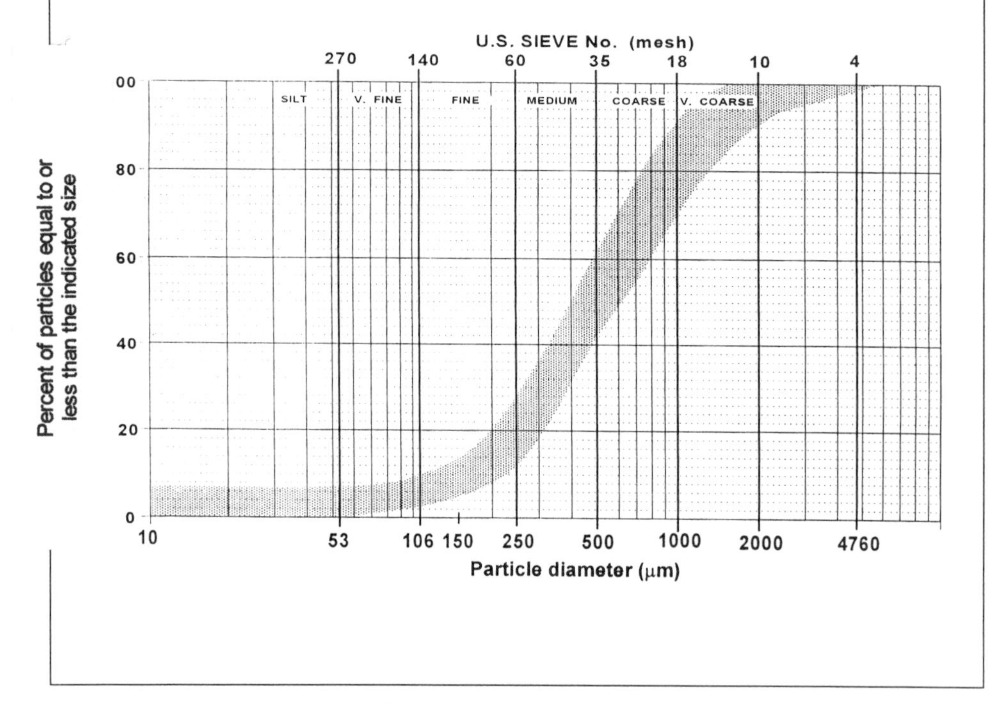

percent organic matter and/or more than 10% carbonates will suggest contamination with significant amounts of subsoil.

In many areas a sandy loam soil does not exist. In these cases the local loam or clay loam soils may be used, but the amount which may be added to satisfy the 8% total silt plus clay limitation will be sharply reduced.

Based on the silt and clay analysis of the soil material a calculation is made of the amount of soil which may be added on a volume basis to the sand. A small sample mix is prepared. Organic materials such as peat moss, compost or other organic wastes may then be added. These organic materials should not exceed 10% by volume of the mix. The organic material chosen should also have a loss-on-ignition value in excess of 85% because some organic sources can contribute significant silt and clay to the mix.

Having prepared the sample root zone mix, it is again subjected to screen analysis to confirm the mix still fits within the particle size envelope (Fig. 8.3). Errors may result where well-aggregated, clay soils are used because the small aggregates of soil will sieve as fine to medium sand.

Having satisfied the criteria of particle size by relatively inexpensive sieve analysis the final selection step is to conduct the relatively expensive porosity and moisture characterization of the sample mix. The accepted ranges of values are listed in Table 8.1.

Table 8.1: The physical properties of a suitable root zone mix.

Criteria	Recommended Range
Total Porosity	35% - 55%
Air-filled Porosity (@ 40 cm tension)	20% - 30%
Capillary Porosity (@ 40 cm tension)	15% - 25%
Saturated Hydraulic Conductivity	15 - 30 cm/hr
Moisture Retention (@ 30 cm tension)	2.5+ cm/30 cm depth

In most circumstances if the selection, based on particle size analysis, has been performed correctly and the criteria for particle size adhered to, the physical properties will fall within the accepted range. If, however, the sample mix fails to pass the one or more of these physical properties, it is advisable to reexamine the mix selected.

Research has shown that a 30-cm depth of the root zone is optimal to provide adequate and rapid drainage (Table 8.2). A shallow root zone does not permit rapid reentry of air whereas a deep root zone rapidly removes too much water due to capillary action.

Table 8.2 The moisture content of a sand root zone of three depths at 2, 24 and 48 hours after saturation.

	Elapsed Time Following Saturation (hr)		
Depth of Mix	**2**	**24**	**48**
(cm)		(% water)	
12	93	79	75
28	85	68	62
43	42	32	24

Installing the Rooting Zone

Pre mixing the sand, soil and organic material off-site is an absolute necessity to insure proper blending of the ingredients. It is not necessary to screen the top soil below 1.25 cm as the larger aggregates act as islands of soil in the sand matrix. Mixing may be adequately performed by front end loaders; adding the materials in the desired ratio by volume of the bucket. Mixing is accomplished by re piling the mix several times. Peat should be moist during the mixing stage to ensure uniform mixing and to minimize peat and sand separation.

It is also a good practice to add 0.6 kilograms of phosphate fertilizer (0-46-0) and 0.15 kilograms of potassium fertilizer (0-0-60) per cubic meter of mix.

Depending on the economics of the particular site the sand:soil mix may be used throughout the entire 30 cm of rooting zone or restricted to the upper 10 cm. The shallower depth of sand:soil mix, may be more expensive due to the need to install two lifts of material. Of course the bottom lift would be the same sand as was used in making the sand:soil mix. It would not be necessary to add organic material to the lower layer.

Sand which is dry has a very low bearing capacity for equipment whereas sand which is wet will carry substantial loads. It is therefore an essential practice to have an irrigation system installed or a portable system working so that the sand is kept wet at all times. It also aids in preventing wind drift of the sand.

The sand:soil mix is dumped at the edge of the field and bladed into rough position with a small bulldozer. Final surface grading may be accomplished with a motor grader. Moving loaded trucks onto the field can result in rutting the gravel layer and intermixing, particularly by unloaded trucks starting up to move off the field after dumping their load.

It is a good practice to have a vertical division between the adjacent soil material at the edge of the field and the sand root zone mix. The sharp break between the two types of material avoids moisture-related growth problems in the future. Strips of plywood or heavy plastic may be used, and moved as the installation progresses.

Sodding, hydro seeding or standard seeding methods may be used to establish the turf. It is essential that the irrigation system be functional before turf establishment is attempted. A standard fertilizer program for turf establishment should be followed.

A quality control program during construction is strongly recommended. Periodic, on-site sieve analysis of the sand:soil mix as it is delivered will insure that the sand conforms to that used in the laboratory analysis and that the field will perform as desired.

Finally, it must be emphasized that a Category I field requires a high level of management skills. Some people have regarded these fields as a large hydroponics system. This may be an exaggeration, nevertheless, the field manager must be very conversant with plant nutrition and water use because the normal buffering (ability to resist change) of soils is missing. A delay of two days in irrigation or postponing a fertilizer application for a week can result in an inferior playing surface.

CHAPTER 9

SOIL ORGANIC MATTER

The previous chapters have dealt with the mineral fraction of the soil and the relationships between the soil minerals, air and water. Mention was made that the total volume of a soil may also contain up to 2.5% by volume of organic matter. While of only minor importance in the total volume of the soil, the organic fraction has an influence on the chemical and physical properties to an extent far out of proportion to the small amount present.

One of the most important components of soil is humus, the product of decaying organic matter. Organic matter was living matter; all plants, animals and bacteria. As living matter is renewed, humus is renewed.

Functions of Organic Matter

Organic matter is the primary factor in increasing the formation and stability of soil aggregates which in turn improve soil porosity and hence the movement of air and water. As an improvement of aggregate stability can be expected from higher levels of organic matter, the problems of soil compaction are also reduced. Furthermore, through the positive influence of organic matter on soil porosity it may increase the amount of plant available water retained in the soil.

It must be remembered, however, that the influence of organic matter on soil aggregate stability only applies to natural soils. Root zones constructed with sand will see little benefit in soil stability from organic matter because sands do not form aggregates. As a result compaction resulting from the breakdown of soil structure will not occur.

Organic matter also influences the chemical properties of a soil. It has a very significant effect on the ability of a soil to retain plant nutrients. This significance is partly due to an increased absorption of potassium, calcium, magnesium and other cations and partly because it becomes a source of all elements required for plant growth as it decomposes. In the latter role organic matter can supply a major portion of the nitrogen and sulphur and 1/3 of the phosphorus required for turf grass production. Organic matter also increases the availability of the micronutrients required for plant growth.

Composition

All decomposing remains of animal and vegetable life contribute to the formation of organic matter in soils. They may be insects, bacteria, fungi, plant tops and roots or organic materials such as peat moss added by the turf manager to the system. Since the origin of organic matter is animal and plant life, the elemental composition of the organic matter is similar to the original living organism (Table 9.1). Of particular importance in the growth of grass is the nitrogen, sulphur and phosphorus contained in the organic matter which may be released for uptake by plants at a later time. During normal soil development some elements may increase in surface soils due to the elements being absorbed from lower depths to be deposited at the surface as plant material decomposes.

Table 9.1: The elemental composition of organic matter.

Element	% on dry wt. basis
Hydrogen	3 - 4
Carbon	52 - 60
Oxygen	32 - 38
Nitrogen	4 - 5
Phosphorus	0.4 - 0.6
Sulphur	0.4 - 0.6

The elements, carbon, hydrogen, oxygen, nitrogen, sulphur and phosphorus, combine to form organic compounds. The same compounds found in plant and animal tissue can also be found in soils.

The organic compounds which have been identified in soil organic matter fall into the following general groups:

- Sugars and Starch
- Amino Acids and Protein

- Hemicellulose
- Cellulose
- Lignin, Fats and Waxes

The type of compounds which are found in the original material influences the rate at which it will decompose As one progresses from the first to the last compound in this list the harder it is for decomposition to take place. Thus simple sugar added to a soil will be broken down in a day or two, whereas cellulose, lignin and waxes may require months, if not years.

Thatch has been found to contain a relatively high proportion of cellulose and lignin, hence it does not decompose as readily as grass clippings and as a result accumulates at the soil surface. Likewise peat moss added to a sand rooting zone can be expected to resist decomposition for one or more years because it also contains a high proportion of cellulose and lignin. Nevertheless, decomposition of these resistant products eventually does take place to form the highly resistant end product of decomposition known as humus.

Humus

Humus is the end product of organic matter decomposition. When extracted from the soil humus is dark brown to black in colour, a feature which generally makes high organic matter soils dark coloured. It has a very complex and variable chemistry, in fact, the true composition has not been fully identified by soil chemists. It has an ability to absorb elements such as potassium and calcium required for plant growth on its surface, thus retaining them from leaching.

Humus has the ability to make some micronutrients such as copper and zinc more available for uptake by plants through a process known as chelation. Many fertilizers contain chelated micronutrients in an attempt to mimic the role of humus in the soil.

Decomposition

The breakdown or decomposition of organic matter is primarily a microbiological process conducted by the wide diversity of microbial life in the soil. Without this ongoing process the surface of the earth would become covered in a depth of dead material and the carbon dioxide, along with other elements, would become tied up and unavailable for future growth of plants.

The environmental factors which control the rate of decomposition of organic matter are the same as those which control the rate of plant growth. Thus, if some environmental factor, such as a rise in spring temperature, increases the rate of grass growth, it also increases the rate of organic matter decomposition. The increasing rate of decomposition will increase the release of nitrogen from the organic matter which is required for the greater grass growth.

Organic matter decomposition requires oxygen as it is essentially a burning process, as a fire, but at a much slower rate. The process may be described by the following equation —

Organic Matter + Microbes + Oxygen = Carbon Dioxide + Water + Microbe Tissue

Removal of oxygen from the system through poor drainage — there are microbes that can live without oxygen — results in incomplete decomposition and the formation of gases other than carbon dioxide, e.g., marsh gas or methane. The formation of peat is a decomposition process where oxygen has been largely excluded by immersion of the dead plant litter in water. Organic matter in poorly drained soils tends to be higher than in well drained soils, in part because decomposition is retarded due to a lack of oxygen. The release of nitrogen and sulphur during the decomposition of organic matter under conditions of low oxygen will be in a form where they are unavailable to plants and where they will be lost from the system.

Since microbes, also a living system, are an essential part of the process, temperature is an important factor in their activity. The optimum temperature for microbial activity in soil ranges from 30 C to 40 C. Most soils under turf will be at the lower end of this range on a sunny, summer day. Decomposition to release nitrogen from organic matter or organic fertilizers, therefore, may not be rapid enough in a cool spring to equal the demands of a grass plant.

Microbial activity is influenced by the pH of the soil. Most microbes function best at neutral to slightly alkaline soil reactions.

The Carbon/Nitrogen Ratio (C/N Ratio)

When organic matter is decomposed under aerobic conditions (adequate oxygen) there is a loss of carbon from the system as carbon dioxide, a gas, and the retention of the nitrogen in the tissue of the microbes or as mineral nitrogen, for example nitrate nitrogen. This process continues until the ratio of carbon to nitrogen remaining in the system reaches a value similar to that of microbial protein. The value is approximately 10 parts of carbon to one part of nitrogen — a C/N ratio of 10. At this point decomposition ceases or becomes very slow because the microbes are essentially now recycling their own tissue. The stable material which remains is known as humus.

The C/N ratio and relative decomposition rate of several materials of interest to turf managers are listed in Table 9.2. With the exception of humus the higher the ratio the slower the rate of decomposition due to a shortage of nitrogen relative to carbon.

Table 9.2: The Approximate C/N Ratio and Relative Decomposition Rate of Several Organic Materials.

Material	C/N Ratio	Decomposition Rate
Sphagnum Peat	100/1	Very Slow
Thatch	70/1	Slow
Grass Clippings	20/1	Rapid
Humus	10/1	Stable

Induced Nitrogen Deficiency

The addition of a large amount of an organic material having a wide C/N ratio, for example, a heavy application of peat moss during the reseeding of a compacted goal mouth area, may result in a temporary nitrogen deficiency in the establishing grass. The deficiency occurs because the nitrogen in the soil is being preferentially used by the microbes in growing new tissue as their population explodes due to the large supply of carbon provided by the peat moss. The condition can be easily corrected by the application of soluble nitrogen fertilizer.

Similar conditions can exist during the establishment of turf on sand root zone systems. Thus it is recommended that no more than 10% of the volume of the upper 15 cm of the rooting zone be peat. It must be remembered that in addition to a potential to induce nitrogen deficiency, the peat will eventually decompose and the space occupied by the peat will be occupied by sand or grass roots

Sources of Organic Supplements

It is generally accepted that peat refers to sphagnum peat obtained from the sphagnum peat bogs in New Brunswick, Quebec and Manitoba. Other sources of high organic material, such as local bogs are also used. These sources should only be used if their content of silt and clay, originating from the runoff water which fed the bog, is less than 10% as determined by a loss-on-ignition analysis.

Other sources of organic material such as peanut shells, sawdust, composted sewage sludge and composted urban wastes may be used. Composted urban wastes are receiving considerable attention as a source of organic matter for both the construction and topdressing of turf. With the exception of sphagnum peat moss, all sources should be tested prior to use to guard against possible chemical contaminants. A simple growth test using ryegrass in pots is often sufficient to indicate there might be a problem.

CHAPTER 10

SOIL NITROGEN

Nitrogen is the principal element responsible for the desirable green colour of turf. Furthermore it increases the growth rate of leaves, stimulates tiller initiation and improves root growth. Although nitrogen is a part of the chlorophyll molecule in the grass leaf, improving the nitrogen nutrition may improve colour more by increasing the rate of emergence of new leaf blades than by increasing the chlorophyll content of the leaf.

Although there are 14 elements required for the growth of grass, NITROGEN is the key to successful grass production. Nitrogen in found in all protein. Protein is fundamental to growth because all enzyme systems contain protein.

Excessive nitrogen, however, can be detrimental to turf. A high level of nitrogen may favour leaf development to such a degree that rooting is decreased. Likewise it may depress the storage of root reserves as more of the photosynthate is channelled into protein, which in turn will favour new leaf growth. Soluble nitrogen compounds may also accumulate in the leaves, which increases the likelihood of disease by being a ready source of nitrogen for the pathogen. The condition of excessive soluble nitrogen accumulation in the leaf is often referred to as increasing the succulence of the plant.

In the previous chapter it was stated that soil organic matter supplied a significant portion of the nitrogen required for turf growth. In the majority of cases, however, the rate of release of nitrogen from the organic matter is not rapid enough to support a vigorous stand; thus the stand becomes thin and prone to weed invasion. In fact, any area of turf not receiving nitrogen fertilizer must depend on the release of nitrogen from the organic matter for its growth.

An interesting comparison of the plant and animal systems is found in their use of nitrogen. Man must obtain his nitrogen as protein, either from a plant or an animal source, in what the chemist calls the reduced form. In contrast a plant cannot use protein nitrogen, but must have its nitrogen in the oxidized nitrate or ammonium form. Nitrate-nitrogen, however, is toxic to man. Whereas 87% of the atmosphere is nitrogen, the animal and plant systems do not have direct access to atmospheric nitrogen but must rely on the essential intermediary which is the soil microbial population to carry out the vital conversions.

The Nitrogen Cycle

The release of nitrogen from organic matter is a dynamic process, dependent on the environmental conditions that influence the diverse population of microorganisms that live in the soil. Many of these environmental conditions are the same as the conditions which influence the growth of grass; such as temperature, moisture and even the supply of nitrogen.

To illustrate the dynamic nature of nitrogen in the soil a diagram known as the Nitrogen Cycle is often used (Figure 10.1). A full understanding of the nitrogen cycle will enable the turf manager to understand the fate of fertilizer nitrogen he may add to the grass.

Central to the operation of the cycle is the soil organic matter. Organic matter contains protein; hence it contains nitrogen. Grass roots cannot absorb the nitrogen as protein, therefore the protein must be converted to a form which the roots will absorb. The nitrogen compound which plant roots absorb is primarily nitrate-nitrogen. The conversion from protein nitrogen to nitrate-nitrogen is carried out by the microbial population. Several organisms break down the organic matter, converting it to amino-nitrogen, then to ammonia-nitrogen. Two very specific microbes, found in all soils, in turn convert the ammonium nitrogen to nitrate-nitrogen.

The two specific microbes carry out the pivotal point in the nitrogen transformations in the soil by a step called nitrification. Nitrification is a two-step conversion of ammonia-nitrogen (NH_4+) to nitrite-nitrogen (NO_2-) and then to nitrate-nitrogen (NO_3-). Very low levels of nitrite-nitrogen are found in soils because it is very rapidly converted to nitrate- nitrogen. In fact, nitrite-nitrogen can be toxic to root growth so it is fortunate that the conversion to nitrate-nitrogen is rapid.

With the exception of nitrate forms such as calcium nitrate, all fertilizer added to the soil must go through this pivotal conversion. The

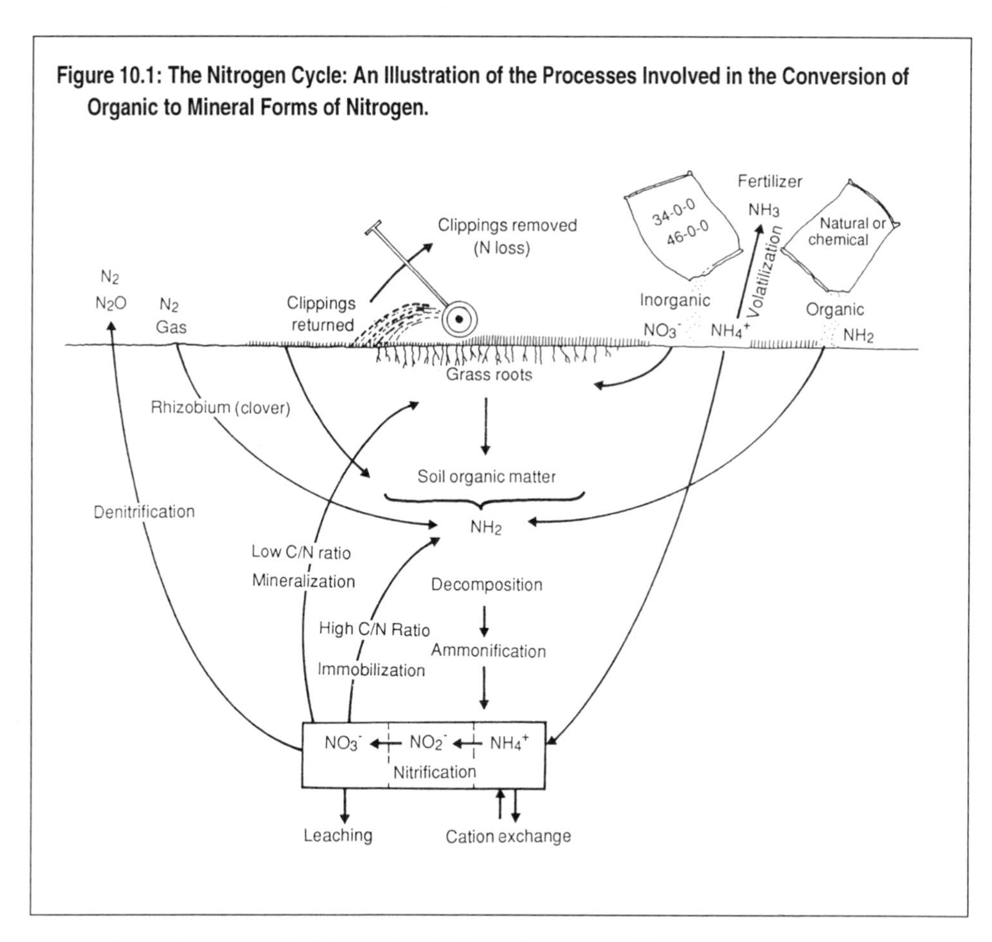

Figure 10.1: The Nitrogen Cycle: An Illustration of the Processes Involved in the Conversion of Organic to Mineral Forms of Nitrogen.

ammonium-nitrogen, which is one half of the nitrogen fertilizer source, ammonium nitrate, must go through the conversion process to be available for uptake by the grass. The oft stated claim that organic sources of nitrogen are nonchemical and hence superior to chemical fertilizers is not the full truth because the soil microbes must convert the organic material to nitrate-nitrogen before the nitrogen is of any value to the grass. The organic sources do, however, have an advantage of restricting the rate of conversion to nitrate-nitrogen because the rate of conversion is dependant on microbial activity, hence a reduction in the potential for leaching.

The reliance on microbial conversion imparts the "slow release" properties on many nitrogen sources. Under favourable conditions of temperature and moisture the conversion of ammonium-nitrogen to nitrate-nitrogen will be complete in 7 -10 days. The conversion of ureaform or Milorgonite to nitrate-nitrogen, however, will take weeks or months, and may never be totally complete.

When nitrogen is in the nitrate form it is highly soluble in water and will be carried downward in the percolating ground water. It should be the objective of every turf manager to not add to the amount of percolating ground water by excessive irrigation. Likewise it should be his objective to minimize the amount of excess nitrate-nitrogen that exists in the rooting zone by careful attention to the rate, frequency and form of the nitrogen he uses.

When nitrogen is in the ammonium form (NH_4+) it is known as a cation, a positively charged ion which may be absorbed by the clay and humus in the soil. In this form the nitrogen is not subject to leaching, however, the soil microbes still have the opportunity to convert it to nitrate-nitrogen which will subsequently be absorbed by the grass, or leached to the ground water.

Nitrogen which is in the ammonia form (NH_3), a gas often called anhydrous ammonia, may be lost to the atmosphere by a process called volatilization. The loss is only of concern where urea fertilizer is the nitrogen source. The process is intensified where urea is applied to grass in warm, humid weather. The volatilization loss can reach values of 12 - 15% of the applied nitrogen. The loss may be avoided by application immediately prior to a rain or where irrigation is applied within 24 hours.

Under poorly drained conditions, nitrogen may also be lost to the atmosphere through a process called denitrification. A group of microbes which flourish in soils devoid of oxygen convert nitrate-nitrogen to elemental nitrogen (N_2) or nitrous oxide (N_2O) which are gases and diffuse to the atmosphere. Thus, good drainage contributes significantly to the efficiency of nitrogen use.

Although a grass plant is not capable of using the bountiful supply of nitrogen in the atmosphere, plants known as legumes can use atmospheric nitrogen. They are plants which have growths, known as nodules, which form on the root. The nodules are the habitat of a special bacteria, *Rhizobium*. The plant serves as the host for the bacteria and through the symbiotic relationship of providing food to the bacteria, the legume plant receives a major portion of its nitrogen from the bacteria in the nodule and hence indirectly from the atmosphere. Clovers are a typical legume. When the clover plant dies and becomes part of the organic matter the nitrogen becomes available to the grass through the decomposition of the entire nitrogen rich plant and the nitrification process described above. The source is of little value to turf managers, however, as they frequently remove the clover as a weed unless the legume is part of a ground cover area.

Induced Nitrogen Deficiency

An important factor in grass nitrogen nutrition is the relative amount of carbon and nitrogen in any organic amendments which may be top dressed onto the turf. The relative amount is commonly referred to as the C/N ratio.

In Table 9.2 of the previous chapter, humus, the stable end product of decomposition, is listed as having a C/N ratio of 10:1. That is, on analysis it will be found to have 10 parts of carbon to every one part of nitrogen. This ratio is approximately the same as found in the microbial cells which break down the organic matter and they are unable to reduce the amount of carbon below the level in their own protoplasm. Whenever the carbon content of the soil is increased above this level microbial activity is also increased because the carbon acts as their food source and they multiply.

When an organic source high in carbon is added to the rooting zone an explosion in the microbial population can occur, if there is sufficient nitrogen available to allow them to generate the protein needed for their cells. When the organic source is low in nitrogen, such as in sphagnum peat, the microbes will absorb the majority of the nitrogen in the rooting zone and the grass will become nitrogen deficient through a process known as immobilization (Figure 10.2). The condition is known as induced nitrogen deficiency and will continue until the C/N ratio drops below 20. To speed up recovery or to counteract the deficiency, supplemental nitrogen in an inorganic form should be added.

When a source of organic matter with a low C/N ratio, such as grass clippings, is added a similar explosion in the population may occur (Figure 10.2). However, no deficiency of nitrogen is seen in the grass

Figure 10.2: The Influence of the Carbon/Nitrogen Ratio on the Soil Microbial Population and the Availability of Nitrogen.

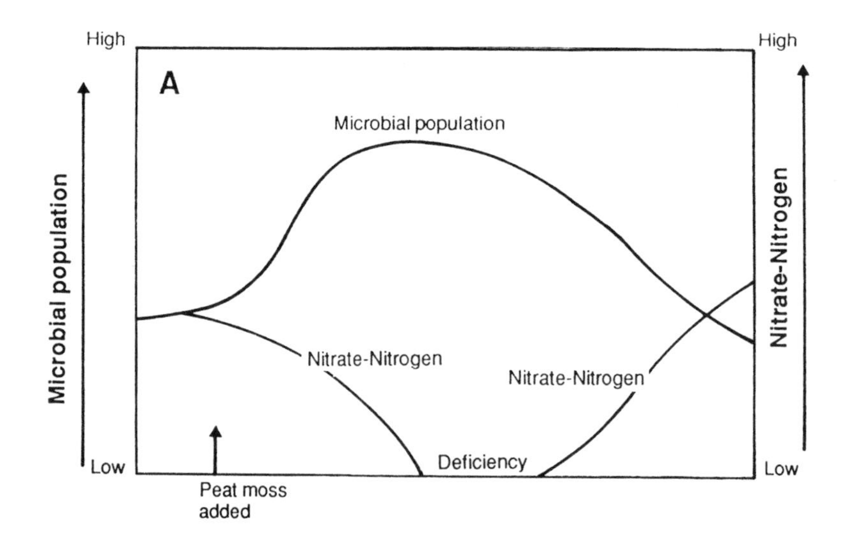

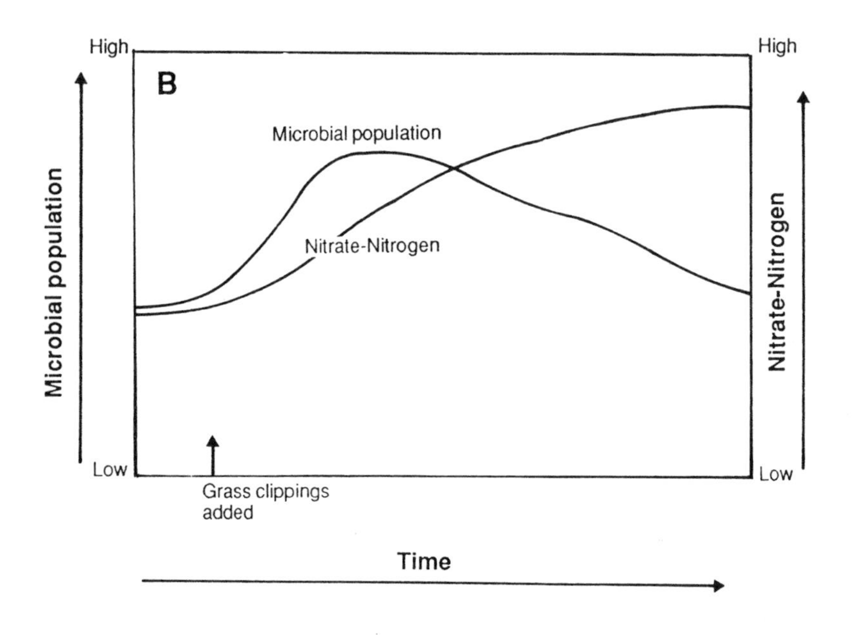

because there is sufficient nitrogen in the clippings to provide the requirements of the microbes without withdrawing any nitrogen from the soil. The process is often referred to as mineralization of nitrogen. As the carbon breaks down and the microbial population returns to normal the extra nitrogen from the clippings returns to the soil, to be utilized by the grass.

Induced nitrogen deficiency may occur where excessive rates of peat are added to a rooting zone mix during construction in order to generate the required porosity and moisture characteristics in the mix. The nitrogen deficiency may be easily corrected by nitrogen fertilizer use. As the carbon is converted to carbon dioxide and lost to the atmosphere, however, the space occupied by the organic matter is backfilled with mineral material and the density of the rooting zone will rise. The short term advantage in porosity and moisture characteristics will disappear and compaction becomes a more serious problem.

Nitrogen Requirement

In general, nitrogen requirements will range from 50 kg N/ha (0.5 kg N/100 m^2) for low use sports fields or rough areas applied once per season, to 200 kg N/ha (2.0 kg N/100 m^2), applied in four to six applications per season for more intensively maintained turf. However, do not apply more than 0.5 kg of actual N/100 m^2 per application. More frequent applications at lower rates are more desirable both for turf growth and to minimize leaching. When clippings are removed, such as on greens, an additional 25 - 30% more nitrogen will be required as significant amounts are removed in the clippings. Older turf requires less nitrogen than younger turf due to a build-up of organic matter from which nitrogen is recycled.

The application rate depends on the nitrogen carrier used. Quick release nitrogen materials such as ammonium nitrate, ammonium sulphate, and urea provide the most rapid response after application, but are more prone to volatilization to the atmosphere or leaching losses. Therefore, their effect may be short lived. Furthermore, quick release carriers have a high burn potential which can cause turf injury through foliar burn when not uniformly applied or where a high rate is used without irrigation.

Slow release nitrogen carriers such as sulphur-coated urea, methylene urea, IBDU, activated sewage sludge, etc., are generally more expensive sources of nitrogen, but provide nitrogen to the plant for an extended period of time. They are less prone to leaching and have a lower burn potential than quick release sources.

Late fall applications of nitrogen are recommended as part of good turf management. The application should be scheduled three to four weeks before the soil freezes. The advantage of this application is earlier initiation of spring growth; often before the soil is dry enough to carry applicator equipment. The nitrogen stored in the plant over winter stimulates the plant to produce more leaves and stimulate tillering which improves recovery from winter diseases. Furthermore the spring flush of growth is less than where nitrogen is applied in early spring, allowing the first application of the year to be delayed until mid-June. Generally a slow release nitrogen fertilizer is desirable for this application to minimize the leaching loss of unabsorbed nitrogen over winter.

Sulphur

Sulphur is a major element required by grass species whose availability is influenced by soil microbial action and series of transformations similar to the nitrogen cycle. While grass requires a concentration level of 0.15 to 0.20 percent in the tissue it is seldom, if ever, found to be deficient due to release from organic matter, sulphur compounds in fertilizer, for example, sulphur coated urea and acid rain.

CHAPTER 11

SOIL REACTION or pH

Much has been written about the soil reaction or pH and many sports field managers lose countless hours of sleep worrying about the results of a lab analysis which indicated a high or a low pH. Understanding what is meant by soil reaction and its implications in grass production can save many hours of that lost sleep.

The practice of liming to sweeten the soil, that is, to raise the pH, predates all other fertilizer practices, even the Christian era. The selection of turf species and the solubility of many plant nutients is influenced by the pH of the soil. That is why most turf specialists, when faced with a nutritional problem, will check the soil pH first, as the medical doctor will check your temperature and blood pressure first when you visit his office.

Soil pH

pH is a measure of the relative acidity or alkalinity of the soil and is measured by a pH meter in negative logarithmic units from 1 (very acid) to 14 (very alkaline). In physical chemistry terms pH is a measure of the hydrogen ion concentration in the soil solution. Therefore, the lower the pH values, the greater the concentration of hydrogen ions. A neutral soil is one that has a pH of 7.0. Because the measuring system is logarithmic, a soil with a pH of 6.0 is 10 times more acid than one with a pH of 7.0. Likewise, a soil with a pH of 5.0 is 100 times more acid than a neutral soil.

Soils in Canada, in their natural state, range in pH from 3.5 to 9.0. The acid soils in Canada are found primarily with sands where coniferous forests have been growing for centuries. Soils of pH 8.5 or greater are usually associated with the saline soils in the prairie regions of Western Canada which may contain a relatively high amount of soluble salts in the parent material.

Most Ontario soils have developed from materials of limestone origin and have a near neutral pH. Most Western Canadian soils also tend to be neutral or alkaline in reaction whereas soils in the Maritime provinces tend to be acid. Therefore, in Ontario most sports field and fairways constructed from local materials can be expected to have a pH near 7.0. An alkaline reaction is usually associated with the sands used for construction or topdressing if they are obtained in Southern Ontario. Sands from the Canadian Shield belt, however, may be acid due to the granites and other igneous rocks from which they were formed.

With the passage of time, usually measured in decades, all soils become more acid. There are five basic factors which contribute to this slow acidification of soils.

- The formation of hydrogen ions during root respiration and microbial breakdown of organic matter.
- The conversion of ammonium-nitrogen to nitrate-nitrogen when ammonium fertilizers are used.
- The addition of elemental sulphur to a soil.
- The breakdown of clay minerals in the soil and the subsequent liberation of aluminum which reacts with water to produce hydrogen. The breakdown speeds up as the soil becomes more acid.
- The leaching loss of calcium and magnesium which have a neutralizing effect on the hydrogen.

Obviously the greater the biological activity such as root growth, the greater the leaching (excess irrigation), the more ammonium fertilizers and elemental sulphur that are added to a sports field, the more quickly it will become acid. In sports fields which contain significant amounts of carbonates, clay and organic matter, however, the acidification is counteracted by a phenomenon known as buffering capacity. The buffering of a soil means the ability of the soil to resist a change in pH. Buffering capacity is due to the cation exchange ability of the clays and humus which will be described in a latter chapter. Sands have no buffering capacity. Therefore, fields constructed on acid sands can become more acid relatively rapidly.

Plant Nutrition and pH

Why is the pH of the rooting zone considered a problem? Primarily because the pH of the soil has a significant influence on the ability of elements required for grass growth to be dissolved in the soil water. If, through a change in pH the elements become insoluble, or soluble at rates less than that required to supply the grass, a pH-derived, nutritional problem may be created. The hydrogen concentration (pH) itself, however, is not a direct problem in plant growth as many plants have been successfully grown at pH 3.0 in solution culture when all the nutrients are provided in a soluble form.

Table 11.1 lists the pH at which the various nutrients required for grass growth is most soluble. With the exception of iron and manganese a neutral pH would be the most desirable.

The most widely discussed problem of pH in soils and its effect on plant nutrition is phosphorus availability. The solubility of phosphorus reaches a maximum between pH 6.5 and 7.2. Above pH 7.2 the solubility decreases due to the formation of relatively insoluble compounds of calcium and magnesium; below pH 6.5 the solubility decreases due to the formation of relatively insoluble compounds of iron, aluminium and manganese. All forms of phosphorus found in the soil have a low solubility in water. It takes time, however, measured in months or years, for the phosphorus to reach the low solubility found in the original phosphate mineral, apatite. Therefore, a program of regular phosphate fertilization, based on an approved soil testing procedure, is a more realistic approach to the pH problem than an attempt to change the pH.

Table 11.1: The influence of pH on the solubility of the nutrients required for plant growth.

Nutrient	Most Soluble pH Range	Least Soluble pH Range
Nitrogen	6.5 - 8.0	5.5 and lower
Phosphorus	6.5 - 7.2	less than 6.5, more than 7.2
Potassium	6.5 - 8.5	6.5 and lower
Calcium	7.0 - 8.5	6.5 and lower
Magnesium	7.0 - 8.5	6.5 and lower
Sulphur	6.5 - 8.5	5.5 and lower
Iron	3.5 - 6.0	greater than 6.0
Manganese	4.5 - 6.5	greater than 6.0
Boron	5.0 - 7.0	less than 5.0, more than 7.5
Zinc	5.0 - 7.0	greater than 6.0
Copper	5.0 - 7.0	greater than 6.0

The lower concentration of nitrogen and sulphur in the soil solution at a pH less than 5.5 is due to the decrease in the population of soil microbes that convert the various nitrogen and sulphur forms in the soil. Iron and manganese increase in solubility as the pH falls. In fact, one of the major reasons for liming a soil is to increase the pH to reduce the solubility of manganese which can be toxic to grass roots at high concentrations.

The four minor elements, iron, manganese, zinc and copper decrease in solubility as the pH rises above 6.0, causing unnecessary concern for field managers whose soils are testing 7.5. The concern is unnecessary in most cases because these are minor elements; elements required in very small amounts for plant growth. Only a few species, grass not being one of them, respond to applications of these minor elements, even at a pH greater than 8.0. If a response is to be found, it will be on sands which are very low in organic matter. Grass species have a very low requirement for boron and it has never been reported as a deficiency problem in turf. However, in saline conditions in arid regions on soils with a pH above 8.0, boron may become soluble enough to be toxic.

Turf Species and pH

The adaptation of turfgrass species is influenced by the pH of the soil environment. Table 11.2 outlines the preferred pH for turf species grown in Canada. While a species may perform very well in monoculture at a pH less than desirable, in the long term the monoculture will be invaded by a more adapted species. As a result Kentucky bluegrass is seldom used in Europe on sports fields where the preferred species are the fescues and ryegrass.

Table 11.2: The preferred pH range for the common turfgrass species grown in Canada.

Species	Preferred pH Range
Kentucky bluegrass	6.0 - 7.6
Colonial bentgrass	6.0 - 7.0
Creeping bentgrass	6.0 - 7.0
Creeping red fescue	5.5 - 6.5
Ryegrass	5.5 - 7.0

Altering the Soil pH

Changing the pH is not a simple procedure. If one wishes to increase the pH of an acid soil to the neutral range, it is necessary to add a liming material; generally calcitic or dolomitic limestone. The dolomitic form of limestone is used where a magnesium deficiency is know to occur because dolomite is a mixture of calcium carbonate and magnesium carbonate. Two other liming materials, quicklime and hydrated lime, may also be used but caution in their application must be taken because they are caustic to the eyes and skin.

Limestone is very slowly soluble in water. Thus, it is necessary to use very finely ground material — 85% should pass a 100-mesh screen. Because it is slowly soluble, it is best mixed with the soil materials for the upper 15 cm of the rooting zone prior to construction of a sports field. Application to an existing field may require several years to show an effect below the first few centimetres. To speed up the penetration of the liming materials into an existing field the applications should be made during a coring operation.

To determine the amount of limestone to apply it is necessary to have a standard pH measurement. If the value is below the desired target pH for the turf, i.e., 6.0, the lab will conduct a second pH measurement known as the "buffer pH" to determine the amount of lime to add. The "buffer pH" measurement reflects the difference in soil buffering capacity of soils due to their varying clay and humus content. For example, a high organic matter, clay soil will require more limestone to change the pH one unit than a sand. The amount of limestone required to raise the pH to the target pH is shown in Table 11.3.

Table 11.3: The lime requirement to correct soil acidity based on the target pH and the buffer pH.

Buffer pH	Target pH = 6.5	Target pH = 6.0
	(tonne material/hectare)	
7.0	2	0
6.5	3	2
6.0	9	6
5.5	17	12
5.0	20	20

There are some turf managers who desire to lower the pH of a soil that is reading 7.8 or greater. It has never been shown that there is an advantage to doing so and the expense is prohibitive. There may, however, be localized horticultural situations where lowering the pH is desirable, such as the growth of azaleas. The materials which may be used are elemental sulphur, aluminum sulphate and sphagnum peat. Sphagnum peat generally has a pH between 2.5 and 3.0. The amount of sulphur or aluminium sulphate required to adjust the pH of the top 15 cm of soil to pH 7.0 is recorded in Table 11.4.

Table 11.4: The amount of elemental sulphur or aluminum sulphate required to lower the pH to 7.0 of soils os three different clay contents.

Initial	Elemental Sulphur			Aluminum Sulphate		
pH	Sand	Loam	Clay	Sand	Loam	Clay
			(kg/100m^2)			
8.0	11.0	22.0	40.7	22.0	44.0	66.0
7.5	6.6	13.2	17.6	11.0	22.0	33.0

In summary, the pH should seldom be a concern for the turf manager. If it becomes excessively high, over pH 7.4, then the turf manager should be alerted to the possible requirement for a higher phosphorus application to satisfy the requirements of the grass. In contrast if the pH falls below 6.0 the manager should be prepared to apply limestone prior to a coring operation. Finally, it must be emphasized that materials to directly alter the pH should never be applied unless a pH determination has been made.

CHAPTER 12

PHOSPHORUS

Phosphorus in Plant Nutrition

During the past century more research effort in time and money has been expended on the study of phosphorous in the soil than any other element. The research reflects the problem of the generally low concentration of phosphorus in soil and its importance in plant nutrition.

Even though the concentration of phosphorus in the grass blade is generally in the range of 0.3 to 0.5 percent, one-eight that of nitrogen or potassium, it is still considered an essential major nutrient. It is essential for the transfer of energy derived from the sun by photosynthesis in the cells in the leaf to all other parts of the plant. The most actively growing portions of the plant, the meristematic region at the base of the leaf and the growing tip of the root, therefore, contain the highest levels of phosphorus. Thus, one realizes the importance of phosphorus in root development.

Phosphorus also tends to concentrate in seeds and on maturation of a plant the phosphorus will move from other parts of the plant to the seed as it is formed. Nevertheless the amount of phosphorus that can be stored in the small seed of bluegrass never fully meets the requirement of the rapid growth that occurs immediately following germination of the seed. Thus there is an essential need for a relatively high level of phosphorus in the soil when a new stand is being established.

Phosphorus seldom influences the colour of turf unless there is an extreme deficiency when a purplish tinge may be seen. Slow development of a newly seeded sports field or slow growth of a turf receiving adequate nitrogen may be a warning that phosphorus is deficient. Any suspicion of low phosphorus nutrition, however, should be confirmed by soil or plant analysis.

Phosphorus in Soils

Most soils generally have less than one ppm of phosphorus in the soil solution at any time. If the rate at which this low level in the soil solution is replaced is too slow there is a deficiency problem and the rate becomes a limiting factor in turf growth. The low level is caused by the extremely low solubility of most phosphorus compounds in water; that is, how fast is phosphorus dissolved into the soil solution.

The original mineral from which all phosphate fertilizers are manufacture — fluorapatite (tricalcium phosphate or rock phosphate) — is extremely insoluble (Table 12.1). The insolubility is further increased by a low level of fluoride in the rock phosphate, a similar concept of using fluoride to increase the strength of tooth enamel. Very finely ground, rock phosphate can be considered a slow release phosphate source, but it is only effective in supplying phosphorus to turf on acid soils; soils of less than pH 5.0.

In the 1880's, two soil scientists, Lawes and Gilbert, at the Rothamstead Experiment Station in England discovered that treating the rock phosphate with sulphuric acid greatly increased the solubility of the material (Table 12.1). The increase was due to the formation of monocalcium phosphate, the basic phosphate compound in ordinary (0-20-0) and triple (0-46-0) phosphate fertilizer. Further manufacturing processes can produce calcium metaphoshate and ammonium phosphates which are essentially water soluble.

Table 12.1: The solubility of several phosphorus compounds.

Compound	Formula	Solubility in Water
		(ppm)
Monocalcium phosphate	$Ca\ (H_2PO_4)_2$	150,000
Dicalcium phosphate	$Ca\ H\ PO_4$	60
Tricalcium phosphate	$Ca_3\ (PO_4)_2$	1.0
Fluor-apatite	$[Ca_3\ (PO_4)_2]_3\ CaF_2$	0.003

Regardless of the form of phosphate fertilizer added to the soil, the phosphate added will slowly revert to an insoluble form through a process often referred to as phosphate fixation. The overriding factor controlling the process is the pH of the soil.

In Chapter 11 it was mentioned that phosphorus was most soluble between pH 6.5 and pH 7.2. At a pH value lower than 6.5 the concentration of aluminum, iron and manganese in the soil solution increases; all elements which form relatively insoluble compounds with phosphorus. At values greater than pH 7.2 there is an increase in the amount of calcium and magnesium in the soil solution; elements which also form insoluble compounds with phosphorus. Hence phosphorus added as a fertilizer tends to remain in a form which can recharge the soil solution most readily in this relatively narrow pH range between 6.5 and 7.2.

It should be understood, however, that the reversion to a completely insoluble form such as tricalcium phosphate is a multi-step chemical process which may take years for completion. In the first few months the initial compounds produced may become only slightly less soluble than the material added as a fertilizer. The greater the amount of these initial forms in the soil, the more rapidly the concentration of phosphorus in the soil solution can be recharged and the greater the fertility of the soil for grass.

Researchers have attempted to increase the efficiency of phosphate fertilizer use by cultivated crops by placing the fertilizer in a band, proving a localized zone of higher phosphorus concentration. To a degree this practice is copied for turf managers in the suggestion that a high phosphate fertilizer should be surface-applied and worked into the top two cm just prior to seeding a new stand.

Phosphorus and Pollution

The chemistry of phosphate in soil, which is based on the formation of compounds of relatively low solubility, is the cause of the very low concentration of phosphorus in the soil solution. Thus, the formation of these compounds prevents any significant downward movement of phosphorus in the soil. Research at the University of Guelph, using radioactive phosphate fertilizer applied in May, demonstrated that the phosphate had not migrated downward more than one cm by the end of the season (Table 12. 2). Pollution by phosphorus in percolating ground water, therefore, seldom occurs.

Table 12.2: The downward movement of fertilizer phosphorus in one season from a surface application on grass.

Depth of sampling	Concentration of applied fertilizer phosphorus
(cm)	(ppm)
0 - 1.5	275
1.5 - 3.0	41
3.0 - 4.5	11
4.5 - 6.0	3
6.0 - 7.5	1

Water pollution by phosphorus from land surfaces is primarily from the erosion of phosphorus-enriched soil particles into water systems. The most effective system for the prevention of soil erosion is a bluegrass sod. Hence phosphorus pollution by surface flow from turf areas is also as close to zero as is feasiblely possible.

Efficient Phosphate Use

A turf manager should be most concerned about the phosphorus levels in his soils at the time of establishment of a new stand. At that time phosphate applied at least at the rate recommended by a soil test is the best insurance move he can make for the rapid establishment of a vigorous sod. This phosphorus should be worked into the top 2.5 cm of soil during the final seed bed preparations.

Subsequent phosphorus applications, of necessity, are applied to the soil surface. Furthermore clippings continually returned to the surface tend to concentrate the phosphorus at the surface. This is not a problem. Research using radioactive phosphorus to identify the source of the phosphorus found in the grass has shown that in one growing season up to 30% of a surface application of fertilizer phosphorus may be utilized by the grass plants. A considerably lower percentage of that applied phosphorus continues to become dissolved in the soil solution in each subsequent year.

While phosphorus only needs to be applied once each season most turf fertilizers contain some phosphorus. The amount required for a full season may be estimated from a soil test. Since the fertilizer rates are generally set by the amount of nitrogen required at any one application, a knowledge of the number of nitrogen applications planned for the year and the rate of material application should allow the calculation of the concentration of phosphorus required in the complete fertilizer.

CHAPTER 13

SOIL POTASSIUM

Most soils contain a relatively large amount of the essential element for plant growth — potassium (K^+) — often as much as 2 percent of the weight of the mineral portion. At the same time the concentration of potassium in the soil solution from which the grass draws its needs may be only 50 to 100 ppm. This relationship illustrates the reason why the total chemical analysis of a soil has little correlation with its ability to supply grass with a nutrient and why soil testing procedures were developed which were closely related to plant growth.

Potassium in soils is an example of a physical chemical property of soil which separate soil materials from inert glass beads as a medium for plant growth. The property is cation exchange. Cation exchange is of equal importance in the fertility of soils as photosynthesis in plant growth.

Potassium in Plant Nutrition

A healthy grass leaf will contain 2.5 to 3.5 % potassium. The potassium in the leaf is not associated with the structure of any specific compound such as protein or carbohydrate in the leaf. It appears, however, as a free ion in the cell sap and functions as an aid in maintaining the ionic and pH balance within the cell as well as with some enzyme functions. In fact, when a leaf dies most of the potassium contained in the leaf will be leached out by the rain and returned to the soil. The release into the soil solution does not require microbial decomposition of the grass leaf.

Potassium in Soil

The major portion of the potassium in the soil is found as an element in the structure of clay minerals and sand grains originating from the minerals known as mica and feldspars in igneous rock. An example of the partitioning of the potassium in a fertile soil is outlined in Table 13.1.

Table 13.1: The partitioning of potassium (K^+) in a fertile soil into categories of relative availability for plant growth.

Form of Potassium	Amount of Potassium
	(kg K^+/ ha.15 cm)
Total K^+	26,000
Relatively Unavailable K^+	23,400
Slowly Available K^+	2,080
Readily Available K^+	520
Exchangeable K^+	468
Soil Solution K^+	52

Over a long period of time, measured in years, if not centuries, the potassium containing minerals, feldspars and mica, break down. The potassium released on this breakdown may become part of the structure of secondary minerals known as clay minerals, or become exchangeable potassium and potassium in the soil solution. The potassium which is part of the clay structure is considered available to slowly recharge the potassium in the soil solution over a period of weeks or months; thus, it is slowly available. The rate at which the restructuring or breakdown of clay minerals releases potassium is known as the potassium supplying power and can vary significantly between soils. Finally, the potassium which is readily available for

Figure 13.1: The relationship between the three major groups of potassium found in a normal soil.

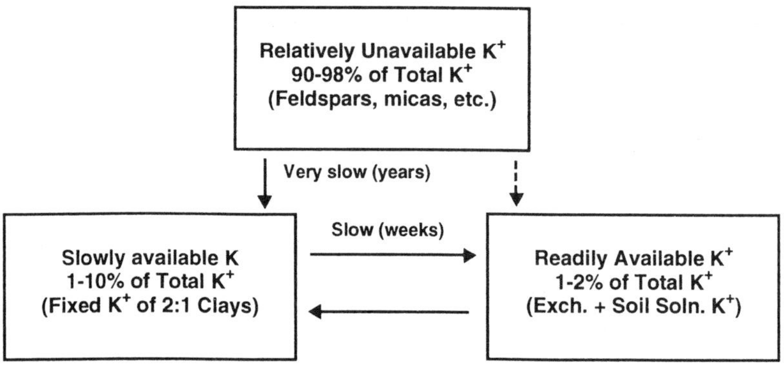

Relatively Unavailable K^+
90-98% of Total K^+
(Feldspars, micas, etc.)

Very slow (years)

Slow (weeks)

Slowly available K
1-10% of Total K^+
(Fixed K^+ of 2:1 Clays)

Readily Available K^+
1-2% of Total K^+
(Exch. + Soil Soln. K^+)

immediate plant uptake is made up of potassium in the soil solution and the exchangeable potassium. These various steps are illustrated in Figure 13.1. Note that the exchangeable plus solution potassium is only a minor portion of the total potassium in the soil.

Cation Exchange

In the above discussion it has been mentioned that exchangeable potassium is potassium associated with the exchange complex of the soil. Cation exchange is a physical chemical phenomenon of compounds or minerals which have a sphere of negative electrical influence surrounding them, resulting in the ability to attract ions which have a positive charge. Cations such as potassium, calcium and magnesium, which carry a positive charge, are attracted by the negative charge in the same manner as the north pole of a magnet attracts the south pole (the general term "cation" is derived from the fact that positive charged ions are attracted to a cathode).

Cation exchange is also a property of large organic matter molecules, particularly when they are in the stable form known as humus, because they also have a sphere of negativity about them. Since clay minerals and humus have a negative sphere of influence and hence have the ability to attract the cations in the soil solution to their surface,

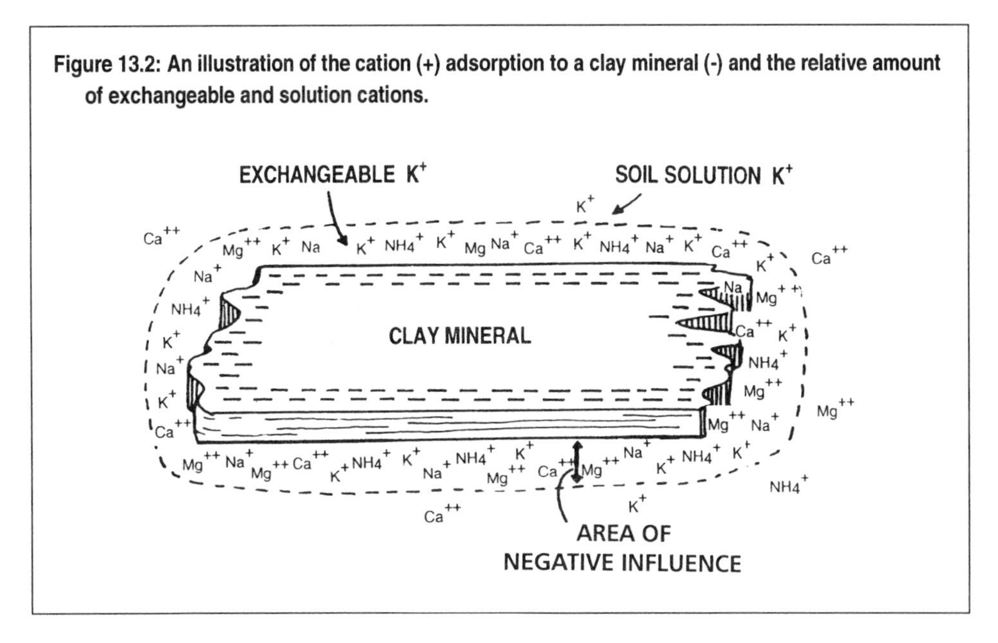

Figure 13.2: An illustration of the cation (+) adsorption to a clay mineral (-) and the relative amount of exchangeable and solution cations.

the cations are held from leaching in the percolating ground water.

Figure 13.2 illustrates the concept of cation exchange. Visualize a clay particle or large, complex organic molecule of humus floating in water (i.e., the soil solution). The clay mineral or organic molecule is negatively charged, the intensity of the charge diminishing with increasing distance away from its surface. In the water surrounding the particle is a swarm of dissolved ions of calcium (Ca^{++}), magnesium (Mg^{++}), potassium (K^{+}), sodium (Na^{+}) and many other cations such as iron, manganese, zinc, and copper which plants require for their growth. When a potassium ion is close to the surface, the negative influence is strongest; as the potassium drifts away from the surface the effect decreases and at some distance from the surface the potassium may finally be considered as free floating or part of the soil solution, that is potassium available for plant uptake. As the composition of the cations in the soil solution changes so does the composition of the ions close to the negative charge.

An illustration of the principle of cation exchange can be found in the operation of a water softener (Figure 13.3). The resin in the softener

Figure 13.3: A common cation exchanger — the home water softner.

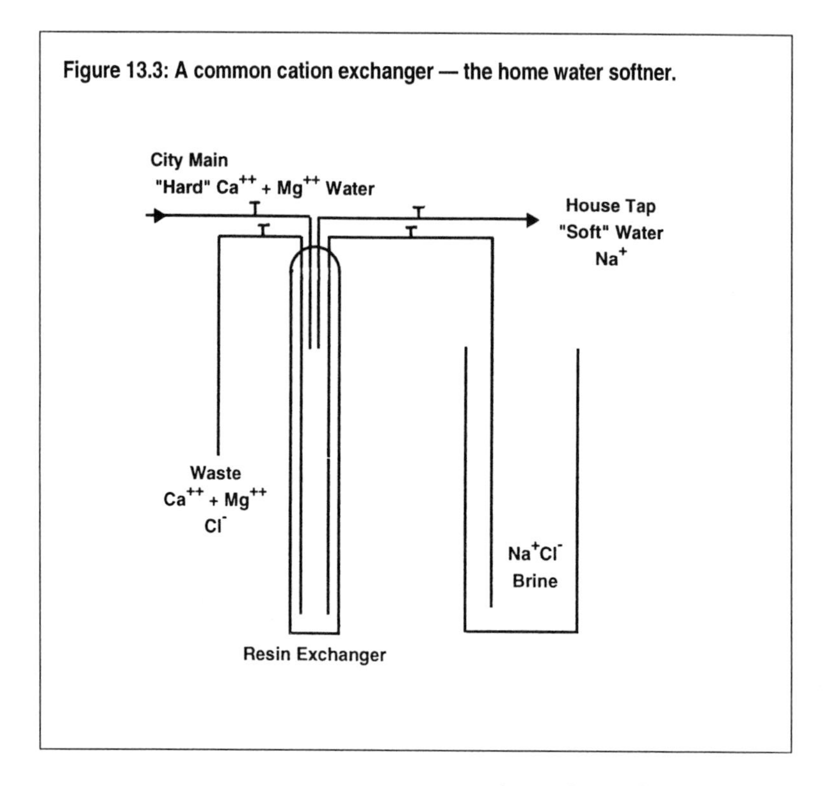

tank is negatively charged. When the resin is conditioned and ready for action the negative charges of the resin are neutralized (covered) with positively charged sodium ions. As the hard water from the city main flows over the resin the calcium and magnesium (ions which create the 'hardness' of water) replace the sodium on the resin because there are many orders of magnitude more calcium and magnesium ions around the resin than sodium. The sodium, therefore, migrates into the water leaving the calcium and magnesium on the resin. The water leaving the tank to the household tap is 'soft' and no longer flocculates the soap.

When the majority of the sodium on the resin has been displaced by calcium and magnesium the water from the softener begins to feel 'hard' again and the resin must be recharged. This is done by back washing the resin with a saturated solution of sodium from the brine tank in which you have placed salt-sodium chloride. And so the cycle is repeated.

The ability of clay and humus to exchange cations has great importance in plant growth. The exchange system acts as the reservoir which prevents cations from leaving the rooting zone in the percolating ground water. It allows the reservoir of elements required for plant growth, such as potassium, to be built up by a regular fertilization program, or, it allows the pH of the soil to be modified through liming.

The use of lime to alter the pH is a further example of cation exchange. As mentioned in Chapter 11, acid soils have a high concentration of hydrogen, aluminum and manganese in the soil solution. Since these elements are all cations, they will be the major ions in the negative sphere of influence. If limestone is added to the soil, the soil solution becomes saturated with calcium ions. When their number become sufficiently large they begin to displace the hydrogen, aluminum and manganese from the clay and humus. As the ion swarm around the clay and humus becomes increasingly saturated with calcium the hydrogen and aluminum is forced away from the negatively charged surface and is washed out in the percolating water. The soil thus becomes increasingly alkaline and the pH rises. As the pH rises the solubility of aluminum and manganese decreases, resulting in an even more favourable environment for grass root growth.

A similar process takes place when potassium fertilizer is applied.

When the potassium fertilizer is dissolved in the soil water, the potassium ions displace calcium and magnesium ions from the clay, building up the level of readily available potassium, hence the fertility, of the soil.

The ability of a soil to retain all cations by the exchange system is called the cation exchange capacity; commonly termed the C.E.C. of a soil. The C.E.C. of a soil depends on the amount of organic matter, the amount of clay and the type of clay found in the soil. The silt and sand fractions do not have a negative charge so they have no effect on the C.E.C.

Soil chemists measure the C.E.C. in the soil in units known as milliequivalent per 100 grams. To compare some soil conditions let us assume the only cation in the soil is potassium. With this assumption the weight of potassium which could be retained under various soil conditions is recorded in Table 13.2. Under Canadian conditions a rough estimate of C.E.C. of a soil is the sum obtained by multiplying the percent clay by 0.5 and the percent organic matter by 2.0.

Table 13.2: A comparison of the ability of humus and types of clay minerals to retain potassium by cation exchange.

Material	Amount of Potassium
	(grams K^+/kg material)
Humus	78
Montmorillonite clay mineral	39
Illite clay mineral	15.60
Kaolinite clay mineral	3.12
Sandy loam low in organic matter	0.76
Sandy loam high in organic matter	3.90
Clay loam having kaolinitic clay minerals	1.56
Clay loam having illite clay minerals	21.45

These values demonstrate the very important role that the decomposition product of organic material, humus, plays in the ability of a soil to retain cations. In a sandy loam soil the increase in organic matter percentage from 1.5% to 6% could result in a 5-fold increase in the C.E.C. Similarly the type of clay mineral which makes up the clay fraction has a large influence. Clays found in the tropics tend to be the kaolinitic types with a low C.E.C. On the other hand clays found in the temperate regions, such as Canada, have illite or montmorillonite type clays and thus are more fertile due to a higher C.E.C.

There is little which the turf manager can do to alter the amount or type of clay in his soil. He can, however, increase the humus content by returning clippings, top dressing with composted organic materials and using management practices which favour a dense, deep root system. Don't look for immediate results because the process of humus enhancement is slow.

Sport facilities constructed on an all-sand rooting medium will have a very low C.E.C. as evident from the above discussion. The lack of any C.E.C. in sand is one of the reasons many designers will advocate the inclusion of a small amount (3 to10%) of natural top soil in the mix. The important factor, however, is the management procedures which will favour the long term build up of organic matter in the sand.

Luxury Consumption

A problem associated with potassium fertilizer use on turf is luxury consumption. When a grass plant is exposed to an abnormally high level of potassium in the soil solution it will continue to absorb potassium to concentration levels in the leaf tissues which are in excess of what is required for normal growth. While not directly harmful, luxury consumption is wasteful if the clippings are removed from the site. Of more concern is the suppression effect the high level of potassium may have on the uptake of other cations such as calcium and magnesium. Where turf is produced on normal mineral soils with an average C.E.C., luxury consumption and depression of calcium and magnesium uptake are not a concern. Where the rooting medium is sand, however, it becomes an additional positive factor when debating the frequency of application or the use of controlled release potassium.

Potassium Fertilization

All potassium fertilizers, with the exception of controlled release forms, are totally water soluble. As a result they can cause foliar burn when applied at a high rate or where there has been an over application due to equipment failure or operator error. It is recommended that not more than 1.0 kg K^+/100 m^2 be applied in any application. Estimating the rate of application of potassium is best done on the basis of a soil test for turf grown on normal soils.

Controlled release forms of potassium fertilizer are becoming available which have a type of coating to delay the release of the potassium. The turf manager must decide the economics of frequent light applications of soluble forms of potassium versus the cost of the coated materials. There is little research available to guide him regarding the application timing of slow release potassium.

Attention to the potassium nutrition of turf growing on a sand system is critical. There will be little reserve in the cation exchange system. More frequent applications will be required. A soil testing system, which measures the exchangeable potassium plus potassium in soil solution, will be primarily measuring the potassium in the soil solution. This potassium may be quickly lost by excessive rain or irrigation and without the reserve of exchangeable and non-exchangeable potassium a deficiency situation can soon arise. Therefore, on a sand rooting system the rule of thumb calls for 3/4 to one kilogram of potassium for each kilogram of nitrogen applied.

CHAPTER 14

TRACE ELEMENTS

There is a saying "a little does a lot, a little more can be a disaster." This saying is most relevant to the use of trace elements.

In previous chapters discussions have been about the major elements required for turf nutrition - nitrogen, phosphorus, and potassium. The concentrations of these elements in the turf tissue are measured in percentage points. Another group of elements essential for turf growth is the trace elements. They are elements whose concentrations in the plant tissue are measured in parts per million.

An often used synonymous term - minor elements - may result in the belief that these elements are of minor importance which is far from the truth. All of the trace elements are essential for enzyme systems in the grass, however, the amount required to make an enzyme functional is very small, hence the more acceptable term — trace elements.

Since the amount required for a specific enzyme function is very small, providing an excessive amount of the same element can often be equally damaging because it may disrupt the function of another enzyme. Therefore, great care must be exercise in the use of trace elements. They should never be applied without proper diagnosis, both visual and chemical, and the application rate should be carefully established.

Those trace elements required for turf production are molybdenum (Mo^-), copper (Cu^{++}), zinc (Zn^{++}), iron (Fe^{++}), manganese (Mn^{++}), and boron (B^-). More recent work has suggested that chloride (Cl^-), cobalt (Co^+) and sodium (Na^+) should be added to the list. From this group iron, manganese, copper and zinc are the elements most likely to be of concern in turf nutrition. Note that many of these elements are cations (+) and may be held by the C.E.C. while the others are anions (-).

As most soils in Canada are of glacial origin and therefore have a very wide range of minerals contributing to their basic mineralogy, the possibility of a trace element deficiency occurring is rather remote. The vast majority of turf managers in Canada will never see any benefit from the use of trace elements.

Potential Problem Areas

There are situations where the probability of a deficiency must be recognized and taken into consideration if a growth problem occurs. These situations are:

- where there is an acid, sandy soil,
- on a muck soil,
- on an over-limed soil,
- on an excessively fertilized soil,
- where excessive irrigation has been used, and
- poor drainage.

Sandy soils, or more particularly sand based sports facilities, are of particular concern due to the very low cation exchange capacity of sands and the low humus content of the root zone. Most of the trace elements are cations, hence are subject to retention and exchange between the exchange complex and the soil solution in the same manner as potassium. With a low exchange capacity loss through leaching becomes a real possibility.

The mineralogy of the sands may also influence the need for trace elements. High carbonate sands originated from materials deposited out of water. The deposition process of the limestone rock from water has provided a good distribution of all elements. Thus, trace elements can be released during the weathering of the limestone sand grains. Sands derived from igneous rock may be more limited in the distribution of trace elements in the sand grains. Furthermore the rate of weathering of the sand grains from igneous rock will be much slower.

In a Chapter 11 the effect of pH on the solubility of nutrients required for plant growth was discussed. The solubility of most trace elements decreases as the pH rises. Hence one would expect trace elements such as iron, manganese, copper and zinc to become deficient where excessive limestone has been added to a soil or limestone derived sand has been used in construction.

Although muck soils are seldom used for sports facilities, soils which have been modified by adding excessive amounts of peat or sand rooting zone mixes containing 20% or more organic material may develop trace element problems. Copper deficiency is the condition most likely to occur in these situations.

While seldom a problem, excessive fertilization can contribute to trace element deficiencies. For example, excessive phosphorus and manganese have been shown to depress the uptake of iron by grass species.

Mismanagement of water, either through excessive irrigation or lack of drainage, may create conditions favourable to trace element deficiencies. Excessive irrigation contributes to the flow of water through the soil, washing out the elements required for plant growth.

Iron

From the group of trace elements the one most likely to show a deficiency is iron. Iron is essential for normal chlorophyll function and in a number of other enzyme functions. As expected, visual evidence of iron deficiency is a light green colour due to a loss of chlorophyll, particularly between the veins in the newly emerging leaf blade. This inter veinal chlorosis is the identifying characteristic which separates the visual symptoms of iron deficiency from nitrogen deficiency.

Normal bluegrass leaves will contain from 300 to 500 ppm of iron on a dry weight basis. Iron is relatively immobile in plants. Thus, the deficiency symptoms will appear first on the newer leaves. The immobility of iron is aggravated by excessively high phosphorus and manganese in the tissue. Thus plants which, by chemical analysis, are considered adequate in iron, may in fact be deficient, because the iron does not move easily to new growth areas.

Iron deficiency is corrected by the foliar application of 6 kg/ha of ferrous sulphate (reduced iron or $FeSO_4.H_2O$) or a soil application of chelated iron. The material should be applied as soon as mixed if hard water is used because the iron is quickly oxidized and made unavailable to the grass.

A foliar application of ferrous sulphate can create a spectacular change in the colour of turf within a few hours. It can also illustrate the fact that an excessive application can be very detrimental because a doubling of the rate may result in blue-black turf in equally as short a time. Repeated iron applications, especially at high rates, have been known to decrease sod density and rhizome development, resulting in turf which has good colour, but thin.

Deficiency Symptoms

As previously mentioned, iron, manganese, copper and zinc are the most probable trace elements to become deficient in turf grasses. The first step in identifying a problem is the observation of a deficiency symptom. The following are some characteristics to look for:

- **Iron** - chlorotic or light green colour between the veins of younger, actively growing leaves whereas nitrogen deficiency affects the entire leaf and appears first on the older leaves,
- **Manganese** - chlorosis of younger leaves with yellow-green to dead spots on the older leaves and a withering of the leaf tip (Note: nitrogen deficiency can also cause the leaf to die from the tip)
- **Copper** - the entire plant becomes stunted and yellow with a bluish appearance to the tips of younger leaves,
- **Zinc** - leaves are reduced in size and grouped together so that the grass has a stunted appearance; leaves may have a darkened appearance.

It is evident from this listing of deficiency symptoms that a definitive visual diagnosis of a trace element deficiency is difficult. Therefore, a suspected deficiency should always be confirmed by plant analysis.

The total concentration of iron in the grass leaf should exceed 50 ppm, manganese should be greater than 15 ppm, zinc greater than 10 ppm and copper greater than three ppm.

If the visual symptoms are verified by the chemical analysis, the next corrective step is to spray a portion of the affected area with the sulphate form of the element at a rate of one or two kg of material/ha.

If this corrects the problem then that trace element, and that trace element only, should be included in the fertilizer to be used on the field.

Fertilizer Materials

Trace element fertilizer materials may be obtained in two forms, as a sulphate salt or as a chelated element. The sulphate salts are all water soluble. Therefore, they may be applied as a foliar spray. Caution must be exercised, however, in their use for foliar applications to avoid foliar burn.

Chelation is the formation of a stable organic complex with the trace element, resulting in a form of the element that is less prone to leaching, but may still be absorbed by the turfgrass roots. Chelated forms of trace elements, such as EDTA-Fe, are more expensive, do not give as rapid a response, but have a longer residual response in the soil than the water soluble sulfates. Other forms of chelated organic molecules are being developed to increase the availability of the trace element to grass plants under high pH conditions. Organic matter (humus) in the soil also has the ability to form natural chelates with trace elements, aiding in preventing leaching of the trace elements from the root zone.

CAUTION

In summary, do not use trace element containing fertilizers unless the appropriate evidence is available that they are needed. Even then use only the element shown to be deficient. Applying a shotgun mixture of several trace elements may create more problems than are solved because while one may be necessary, the others in the blast from the gun may disrupt the nutrition of the grass from another aspect.

CHAPTER 15

THE FERTILIZER ACT

The Act

Turf managers in Canada are fortunate to have a Federal Government Act to regulate, from coast to coast, the sale of materials used to provide plant nutrients for turf.

The Act, "for the regulation and control of agricultural fertilizers" is administered by the Plant Products Division, Fertilizer Section, Agriculture Canada. Every turf manager should have a knowledge of the implications of the Act.

The Act states that "no person shall sell, or import into Canada, any fertilizer or supplement unless the fertilizer or supplement has been registered as prescribed, conforms to prescribed standards and is packaged and labeled as prescribed." Essentially this statement means the user is protected against potential health hazards, fraud in marketing, and is provided with a fair marketplace and has the assurance of the purchase of effective products.

The act interprets a fertilizer to be "any substance or mixture of substances containing nitrogen, phosphorus, potassium, and other plant food, manufactured, sold or represented for use as a plant food." On the other hand, the Act interprets a supplement to mean "any substance or mixture of substances, other than fertilizer, manufactured, sold, or represented for use in the improvement of the physical condition of the soil or to aid plant growth or crop yields."

The label on a fertilizer container is an important item because it contains much valuable information on the correct use of the material. The label is defined to mean "any legend, word, mark, symbol or design applied or attached to, including in, belonging to or accompanying any fertilizer, supplement or package."

The Act divides the plant nutrients into two categories — major plant nutrients which are nitrogen, phosphorus, and potassium, and lesser plant nutrients which cover all the remaining nutrients required for plant growth. Organic matter in fertilizers refers to "substances of animal or vegetable origin remaining after removal of the moisture and ash fractions" (ash means mineral material).

Fertilizer Grade

An important part of the label is the grade which refers to the minimum percentage on a weight basis of total nitrogen, available phosphoric acid and soluble potash, in that sequence, that is in the fertilizer. The grade is represented by three number which appear on the bag (see Fig. 15.1).

24 - 4 - 12.

Thus, a 25-kg bag of this material would contain 24% (6.0 kg) total nitrogen (N), 4% (1.0 kg) of available phosphoric acid (P_2O_5), and 12% (3.0 kg) of soluble potash (K_2O).

A somewhat strange convention is found in the system of reporting the plant food content of fertilizers. It originated from the methods used by chemists in reporting analysis in the 19th century. Nitrogen was determined by a procedure known as the Kjeldahl method for total nitrogen and is reported as total N. Phosphorus was extracted from the phosphate rock with citric acid and was supposed to represent that fraction of the phosphate in the rock which was available to plants.

Figure 15.1: A drop-type and a rotary spreader for the application of fertilizer. Note the grade numbers on the bag.

24-4-12

Thus the terms "available phosphoric acid"', or sometimes "citric acid soluble phosphate" is used. The chemists in those days always reported their analysis in the form of the oxides of the element, hence phosphorus was reported as P_2O_5. The fertilizer industry has retained the format because an analysis of 20% P_2O_5 looks better than 8.7% P. Likewise potassium, which is soluble in water, is reported as soluble potash and as the oxide, K_2O. The method of analysis used to determine the grade is carefully monitored and is the latest method published and approved by the Association of Official Analytical Chemists (AOAC).

A category of nitrogen, recognized as important in the turf industry is called "water-insoluble" nitrogen. This fraction of nitrogen is of particular interest for slow-release materials. It is important to remember the category only applies to the nitrogen fraction of the fertilizer. Specific procedures have been established by the AOAC for the determination of "water-insoluble" nitrogen.

To protect the farming population in the early days of fertilizer use from companies selling low analysis materials such as a 2-8-8, the Act requires that all fertilizers will contain not less than 24% of the major plant nutrients, nitrogen, phosphorus, and potassium. There are exceptions to this regulation, however, and they are

- a customer-formula fertilizer,
- a specialty fertilizer, or
- a fertilizer, the ingredients of which contain
  (1) at least 50% animal or vegetable origin suppling 25% of the nitrogen in the mixture in a water-insoluble form, and
  (2) at least 18% major plant nutrients combined.

A customer-formula fertilizer is defined as "a fertilizer prepared in accordance with a written formula that sets forth the name, amount and analysis of each ingredient, the fertilizer grade of the total mixture and the signature of the person for whose use for fertilizing purposes it has been prepared." It means you can formulate a fertilizer for your specific use and have a company prepare a "bulk blend" of the material without subjecting it to the 24% rule. It is for your use only, not for resale.

A customer-formula fertilizer which contains a pesticide that is registered under the Pest Control Products Act is exempt from the registration only if the manufacturer (blender) provides the regional office of the Agricultural Inspection Directorate with

- a copy of the label or bill of sale, and
- the name and address of the customer for whose use for fertilizing purposes the fertilizer was prepared.

A "specialty fertilizer" means a fertilizer recommended for use

- on household plants, urban gardens, lawns, golf course and nurseries,
- in greenhouses, or
- as a source of lesser plant nutrients only (micro nutrients).

This regulation is the reason that many of the turf fertilizers, such as 7-7-7, have been offered for sale. It would not fit the 24% rule, but the low analysis makes the potential for foliar burn and irate customers highly unlikely.

Other materials which are exempt from registration under the Act are the supplements sold for the correction of soil acidity and basicity. Thus, limestone materials are not controlled by the Act. Furthermore organic materials such as peat, peat moss, sphagnum peat, bark, saw dust and other fibrous material sold for the improvement of the physical condition of the soil are not covered.

The 1985 revision of the Act addressed the registration of fertilizers containing slow release nitrogen. Section 10.3 of the Act states "a mixed fertilizer that is represented on its label as a slow release fertilizer consisting of Isobutylidene diurea (I.B.D.U.), urea formaldehyde, urea-form, or any other chemical compound having similar slow release properties will contain at least 25% of the total nitrogen guaranteed present in the water-insoluble form".

The inclusion of micro nutrients is also regulated. Where the label on a fertilizer or representations made in respect of a fertilizer indicate that the fertilizer contains a micro nutrient such as boron, copper, zinc, molybdenum and manganese the Act states

- such plant nutrients will be present in sufficient quantity in the fertilizer to be efficacious for the purpose or purposes indicated on such label or in such representation; and
- such plant nutrients at recommended rates will not be present in toxic amounts.

Further, the Act requires the label contain the following cautionary statement;

> "CAUTION: this fertilizer contains (*specify name of lesser plant nutrient*) and should be used only as recommended. It may prove harmful when misused."

Concerns about infractions of the Act should be addressed to the local office of the Plant Products Division of Agricultural Canada (blue pages in your phone book). If you register a complaint, inspectors from the Division will do the sampling of the product and submit it to the appropriate laboratory for analysis. They will also require shipping bills etc. Therefore, keeping a file on fertilizer materials purchased is essential.

To further protect the gullible, fertilizers represented to be used for foliar or seed application must have the following statement on their label "only minor amounts of nutrients applied to foliage or seeds are absorbed by plants. Foliar and seed treatments, therefore, supply only a portion of the three major nutrients (nitrogen, phosphorus, potassium) required for successful crop production. Such a product is recommended only for use as a supplementary source of plant nutrients to a basic fertilizer program that relates to the fertility level of the soil."

For further information obtain a copy of "Guidelines to the Fertilizers Act" from your Plant Products Office.

As a result of the regulations of the Fertilizer Act, a fertilizer industry has developed in Canada which is highly professional and which provides the user with reputable products. Nevertheless there remains a fringe group who promote materials of dubious, if any, benefit to the turf. Always ask for their registration under the Fertilizer Act. If none is forthcoming, put your cheque book back in your pocket.

CHAPTER 16

ESTIMATING FERTILIZER NEEDS

Does a visit from your fertilizer salesman leave you bewildered? Do you know the facts about the materials or do you rely on the salesman for your information? The final decision should be based on price.

What are the questions you should be asking yourself as you listen to the sales pitch from your fertilizer salesman? Some might be

- Should I use an organic or an inorganic?
- Should I use a slow release or soluble source or a mixture of the two?
- Should the nitrogen be as a nitrogen only carrier or a mixed fertilizer?
- What time and rate of application should I use?
- What analysis should I buy?
- What price should I pay?

Pricing Fertilizer

As stated in the previous chapter fertilizer generally consists of one or more of the three major nutrients — nitrogen, phosphorus and potassium. In the production of turf, however, the principle reason for purchasing fertilizer is to supply the turf with nitrogen. In many cases, if the turf manager has the benefit of a soil test for phosphorus and potassium in making his decision, he will find that for most applications he only needs a nitrogen fertilizer.

How does one compare nitrogen carriers on the basis of price? It is totally erroneous to compare carriers on the basis of cost per tonne. Such a comparison is analogous to the proverbial comparison of apples and oranges. Apples and oranges are both round, yet even their skins are as different as are their tastes. In a comparison of nitrogen carriers it is obvious they all contain nitrogen, but that nitrogen may be in a different chemical form, it may be slow release, it may have a high potential for foliar burn, etc. But of greater importance a comparison on the basis of price per tonne can be erroneous because of the different nitrogen analysis of the various carriers.

The most precise way to compare the cost of nitrogen carriers is to calculate the price per unit of nitrogen (cents/kg N) in the carrier.

An example calculation for a 30-0-0 material valued at $300.00/tonne is:

$$\frac{\$300.00}{\text{tonne}} \times \frac{\text{tonne}}{\text{1000 kg}} \times \frac{\text{100\% 30-0-0}}{\text{30\% N}} \times \frac{\text{100 cents}}{\$} = \text{100 cents/kg N}$$

This calculation, which at first appears daunting and time consuming, may be simplified and use for any nitrogen material by multiplying the price/tonne by 10 and dividing the product by the percent nitrogen in the carrier.

Table 16.1 provides a comparison of some commonly used materials for turf fertilization based on some 2000 prices. The data illustrate that urea is the cheapest form of nitrogen available, followed by ammonium nitrate. Note that while urea costs more per tonne it is actually cheaper per kilogram of nitrogen. This is due to the higher analysis.

Table 16.1: A comparison of some nitrogen sources on the basis of the cost per tonne and the cost per kilogram of nitrogen.

Carrier	Analysis	$/tonne	Cents/kg N
Ammonium Nitrate	34-0-0	305.00	89.7
Urea	45-0-0	330.00	73.3
Sulphur Coated Urea	32-0-0	600.00	187.5
I.B.D.U.	31-0-0	1700.00	548.4
Organic (Turkey Litter)	5-2-4	856.80	1713.6
Farm Grade Mix	20-10-15	264.00	132.0

When compared with ammonium nitrate and urea forms there is a dramatic increase in the cost of each kilogram of nitrogen for the slow release forms. In general within the slow release group the more complex the chemistry of the manufacturing process the higher the cost of the nitrogen.

If a comparison is made. between two organic sources, I.B.D.U, a manufactured organic source, and Turkey Litter, a natural source, on the basis of price per tonne the Turkey Litter would win. Placing the comparison of the carriers on the basis of the price per kilogram of nitrogen, however, leaves I.B.D.U. the winner by three times.

Other Considerations

There are many situations where low use turf only requires a yearly shot of one or two nitrogen/ 100 m^2. A farm grade material may be the answer. Using the price comparison in Table 11.1 it would be $0.55 less expensive per 100 m^2 to apply one kilogram of nitrogen as 20-10-15 than to use sulphur coated urea; while at the same time you would be applying 0.5 kg of phosphate and 0.75 kg of potassium at no additional cost.

With today's technology it is possible to produce high quality turf applying 0.5 kilograms of nitrogen/100 m^2 as urea with a pneumatic (airflow) spreader followed immediately by a light irrigation. Substitution of low-cost urea for relatively high cost slow release material, however, has an added cost of more expensive equipment for application and management skills to program the use of soluble nitrogen.

The quality of turf is primarily controlled by the management of nitrogen. As no valid soil testing procedure exists for nitrogen, the amount and frequency of application must be judged by the turf manager to give the colour and vigour he desires.

Estimating Phosphorus, Potassium and Lime Requirement

The most accurate tool available for turf managers to determine soil pH, phosphorus and potassium requirement is the use of the soil test. The soil test serves as an important reference or guide line from which to base phosphorus and potassium additions as it reflects the amount of these elements or lime which must be added to achieve optimum growth of the turf species. The actual rates of lime, phosphorus or potassium to apply may be obtained from your provincial soil testing service, your local turf specialist or your fertilizer dealer.

Proper sampling is important; the results are no more accurate than how representative the sample is of the sports field (Fig. 16.1).

Figure 16.1. The necessary steps and equipment required for soil sampling.

1. The basic tools for obtaining a soil sample for analysis: a soil sampling tube, plastic pail for collecting and mixing, soil sample containers and recording material.

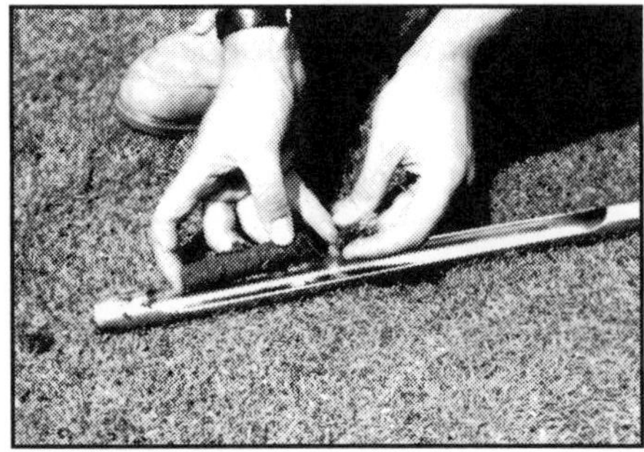

2. Most sports fields should be sampled to 15 cm, however, a depth of 7.5 cm is best for bowling greens. Remove the thatch layer before placing the core in the collection pail.

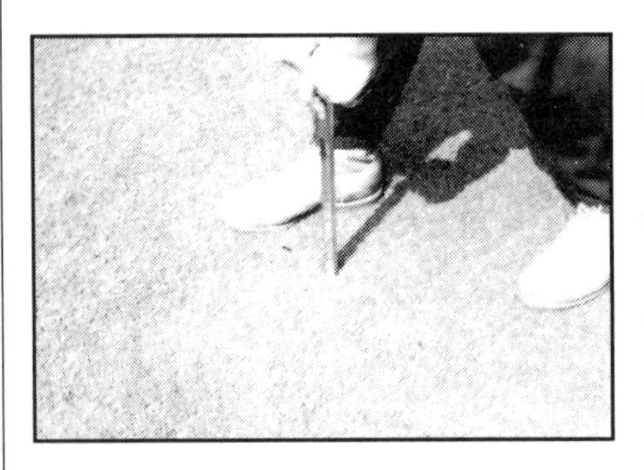

3. Each sample should consist of at least 15 cores which are thoroughly mixed in the pail.

4. Place a portion of the well mixed soil in the sample box, assign the box a number corresponding to the number on the record sheet and a sampling map.

There are five steps which should be followed in obtaining a representative sample.

- **Step one** is to acquire the tools and materials. A soil sampling probe is a convenient tool for taking soil samples. If a probe is not available, a cup changer or shovel may be used. A clean plastic pails should be used to collect and mix the sample. Have available a supply of sample bags, boxes and information sheets which are available from soil testing laboratories, county agricultural offices or your turf specialist.
- **Step two** is to sample the correct depth and frequency. Bowling and golf greens should be sampled to a depth of 7.5 cm as this is the depth where the root feeding zone of bent grass is most active. Other sports fields can be sampled to a depth of 10-15 cm..Take at least ten to 15 cores from each green or field. The more cores, the better the sample represents the soil conditions on the field. Any specific problem areas should be sampled separately.
- **Step three** is to remove the thatch layer from each core before placing them in the pail for thorough mixing. It is not necessary to dry the sample.
- **Step four** is to place a sufficient sample in a plastic bag to fill the sample box. Ship the sample boxes, together with any required fee, to the analytical laboratory of your choice.
- **The fifth and most important step** is record keeping. Keep a record of sample numbers and a map of the location of sample areas and where special samples were taken. Provide complete and accurate information on the information sheets which should accompany the soil samples and be sure to specify the type of turf for which a recommendation is requested. Keep a record of all soil analysis data and fertilizer applications made on a field. These historical records are valuable in the interpretation of fertility problems which may occur in the future.

Granular fertilizers are applied by broadcasting with centrifugal type spreaders or drop type spreaders (see Chap. 15, Fig. 15.1). For accurate applications the spreader must be calibrated to ensure the correct rate of application and the machine maintained in good condition to provide uniform fertilizer distribution. Granular fertilizer should always be applied when the turf foliage is dry. Applications of materials with a high burn potential should be timed to occur just before natural precipitation or scheduled irrigation to move the fertilizer down into the root zone. An application rate below 0.125 kg N/100 m^2 of granular materials to bentgrass may result in a mottled or freckled appearance due to uneven distribution

Granular fertilizer applied to closely mowed bentgrass may result in considerable fertilizer being removed in the mower basket. Leaving the baskets off for one or two mowings, the use of fine grade, granular materials or liquid formulations are application systems which will avoid the loss.

CHAPTER 17

TOPDRESSING

Since the early observation on dune areas several reasons have emerged for topdressing. The reasons are: thatch control, soil modification, smoothing and levelling, covering of bentgrass stolons, covering of seed during overseeding, recycling organic wastes through composting and winter protection. Two of these reasons, thatch control and soil modification will be covered in some detail.

The concept of topdressing originated when it was recognized that creeping bentgrass growing on coastal dune areas spread faster and was more dense when covered by the drifting sand. This observation was applied to golf and bowling greens where it has the added advantage of levelling the surface and improving the ball roll.

Thatch Control

Thatch is defined as the accumulation of living and dead leaves, roots and stems and other organic debris between the soil surface and the base of the green vegetation.

Thatch is a major problem on bentgrass greens and fairways. It does not present a problem for most sports field management programs, although lightly used areas on a field, such as corners may have a significant build up of a thatch layer.

Why worry about thatch? It should only make the surface more resilient which is an advantage on a field used for contact sports such as football. On the other hand thatch influences the quality of the turf by creating localized dry spots, increasing scalping during mowing, and increasing the potential for disease, insect and winter injury.

Studies have demonstrated that topdressing is one of the most efficient procedures available for thatch control (Table 17.1). In this experiment topdressing was done monthly with the soil indigenous to the site at a rate of 0.1 $m^3/100\ m^2$. The data was recorded after 10 topdressing operations over two years. Although cultivation reduced the depth of thatch, topdressing alone was more efficient for the control of thatch than any of the cultivation procedures which are more costly and time consuming.

Substitution of topdressing for turf-damaging verticutting or coring has the additional advantage of not opening up the turf sward to allow the germination of weeds. Annual bluegrass may not be as prevalent in topdress-only situations as where some form of cultivation is used which opens up the cover and assisting in the germination of the annual bluegrass seed.

Table 17.1: The influence of topdressing and cultivation on the control of thatch in bentgrass maintained as a putting surface.

Treatment		Without Topdressing	With Topdressing
		(mm of thatch)	
Control	11.5		
Topdressing Only	4.2		
Vertical Mowing		9.4	4.0
Core Cultivation		8.1	4.9

Topdressing is often recommended for the modification of the root zone as well as levelling and smoothing the surface. The latter are accomplished by matting the surface after the topdressing operation.

Topdressing Material

A cardinal rule in topdressing is to topdress with the same material as was used in the construction of the existing root zone. If this rule is not followed it is impossible to predict what water transmission and retention values may develop with time as diverse layers of sand:soil mixes builds up. Coring to relieve compaction, followed by topdressing with a non-compatible mix may, over a period of time, result in a clay:silt:sand ratio which will compact to a greater degree than the original material.

If the original rooting zone was a clay, a saturated zone may occur within the topdressing layer following a heavy rain or irrigation. Similarly a saturated zone may eventually develop due to a perched water table if the original root zone was constructed from a sand having a significantly different size distribution than the topdressing sand. The worse scenario is to topdress a sand rooting zone with a silty clay soil which will eventually plug the pores in the sand and ruin the advantages of a sand rooting zone.

Because of the time, generally several years, required to modify the particle size distribution of a root zone, the danger of incompatibility of particle size of the original material with the topdressing material and the restriction of the depth of the new root zone to the depth of coring, it is not recommended that topdressing be used as a procedure for field renovation. It is better to "bite the bullet" and carry out a complete field renovation at which time corrections of any drainage problems can also be achieved.

Where the sole purpose of topdressing is to reduce the organic matter content at the soil surface, i.e., the depth of thatch, it is advisable to use a low organic matter material. Thus, there is a preference for pure sand as a topdressing material. The sand should contain less than 10% 0.125 mm particles and should have 80% of the particles in the 0.125 to 0.50 mm range.

The rate and frequency of topdressing is generally dictated by the amount of thatch accumulation. A general practice is to use four to six applications per year on intensively used turf or where thatch is more than 2.0 cm deep. The rate may vary between 0.3 and 0.6 mm per application. Table 17.2 converts the depth of application to volume of material required per 100 m^2. Light topdressing at a rate of 0.3 mm every two weeks may be necessary if a new bowling green is being levelled. Most turf situations, however, may only require a topdressing of 0.6 cm inch twice each season to control thatch. The operation should be coordinated with periods of rapid tiller development and with the time of overseeding.

Table 17 2: The volume of material required to topdress 100 m^2 area to various depths.

Depth of Topdressing	Volume of Soil
(mm)	(cubic meters)
0.3	0.3
0.6	0.6
0.9	0.9
1.2	1.2
1.8	1.8

Topdressing may be used as a means of disposal of composted organic wastes from other parts of a grounds maintenance program. High capacity topdressing equipment (Fig. 17.1) has made the procedure rapid and economical. Furthermore tipping costs at the local landfill site can be greatly reduced.

A factor which should be considered in the selection of topdressing materials is freedom from weeds. Obvious contaminants such as quack grass rhizomes should be ample reason to reject a supplier. Freedom from other weeds may be checked by a simple germination test. Freedom from herbicides used on the field where the topsoil was

Figure 17.1: A tractor drawn topdress applicator capable of high volume application of sand and organic materials to a sports field.

obtained should also be considered. A final consideration should be freedom of the material from stones and other debris, such as broken glass, which might cause injury to the athlete.

A noted Canadian golf superintendent once remarked "You can tell the number and duration-of-tenure of superintendents at any golf course by the number and depth of the sand layers in the surface of the green". The same may also be said for some sports fields.

CHAPTER 18

MOWING

The mowing of turf is a complex issue involving the interaction of height, frequency, mowing equipment, species, stress and turf use.

Mowing is detrimental to turf species as it drastically changes the normal reproductive physiology of the grass plant from one which is designed to reproduce by seed with secondary tillering to a plant which relies entirely on tillering. Root growth, carbohydrate production and storage, disease incidence and water relationships are all affected. Yet the species survives and prospers when continually mowed at 5 cm or less.

Mowing Height and Frequency

Mowing height and frequency requires a balance between beneficial and adverse effects. Mowing increases turf quality through better tillering, thus providing more shoots per unit of ground area. On the other hand, mowing decreases root growth due to the removal of leaf blades which in turn reduces photosynthesis. Mowing decreases tolerance to stress including wear from play, drought, high and low temperatures, disease and weed competition.

A knowledge of the location of the growing point or meristematic region is essential in the understanding of the physiology associated with mowing of turf grasses. The meristematic region is that section of the plant where active cell division occurs. In dicots (a plant group to which many weeds belong) the growing point associated with stem elongation is located at the tip of the plant so that the youngest leaves are at the top of the stem. In the monocots (the group to which turf grasses belong) the growing point seldom moves above the soil surface, except where seed head formation occurs. New leaves are continually produced by lateral bud development around the growing point and each individual leaf elongates by cell division in a region at the base of the leaf, know as an intercalary meristem. As these cells enlarge and mature, the leaf elongates. Thus the mower is cutting of the oldest part of the leaf while new leaf tissue is being formed at the base (Figure 18.1).

Fig. 18.1: A schematic representation of the meristematic region in a turfgrass tiller from which new growth originates.

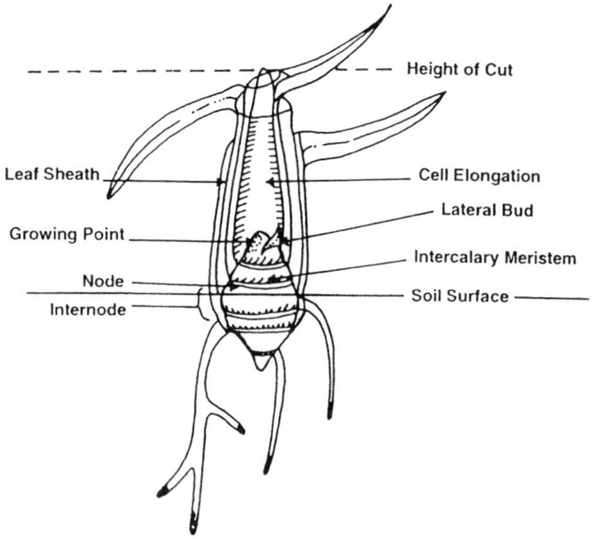

The intercalary meristem of an individual leaf remains active in cell division for only a short time (weeks) so that by the time the leaf becomes visible most of the cell division has ceased. Cell enlargement or growth of each cell continues, however, forcing the sheath and the leaf higher, requiring the cutting of the turf. Mowing so close to the soil surface as to damage the intercalary meristematic region results in what is called scalping and death of the plant.

The repetitive removal of the top of a grass plant disrupts the normal procedure for the seasonal development of the plant. Normally, at the commencement of spring growth, one or more of the principle tillers existing at the base of the plant begin a process of internode elongation, elevating the growing point above the soil surface. Elongation of the stem is designed to elevate the seed head above the leaf canopy to promote flowering, pollination and seed dispersal. Under most turf conditions, with the exception of annual bluegrass and some cultivars of bluegrass and ryegrass, stem elongation never occurs and the plant remains in an unnatural vegetative condition throughout the season; in other words during a major part of the year it is under a stress of forced vegetative reproduction. Turf grasses, however, have developed varying degrees of tolerance to repeated removal of top growth as pasture grasses have developed varying degrees of tolerance to repeated close grazing.

Vegetative reproduction is a desirable means by which the density of the stand is increased by tiller development from lateral buds at the base of each tiller. Both mowing height and frequency have an impact on the degree of tillering that is obtained. Mowing, in removal of the older part of the leaf, removes the section responsible for hormone production which suppresses tiller development. Furthermore, the amounts of tillering induced by mowing will be greater during those periods of the year when the plant would not normally be attempting seed production —- fall and very early spring.

Table 18.1: The weight of green material (verdure) remaining following mowing Kentucky bluegrass at several heights.

Height of Cut	Fresh Weight/10 m^2
(mm)	(gram)
7.6	1.5
12.7	2.5
19.0	12.5
38.1	20.5
63.5	27.5

(From: Madison, J.H. (1971) "Practical Turfgrass Management" Van Nostrand Reinhold Co., Toronto)

Table 18.2: The influence of mowing height and moisture content on the impact resistance (hardness) of bluegrass on a sandy loam soil.

	Relative Moisture Content	
Mowing Height	Wet	Dry
(cm)	(meters/sec^2)	
3	497	773
9	518	740
15	529	720

(From: Zebarth, B. (1984) M.Sc. Thesis, University of Guelph)

Increasing the mowing height will obviously increase the amount of the plant remaining above the soil surface (Table 18.1). Increasing the amount of material remaining after mowing would be expected to enhance the resiliency or cushion for the athlete on a sports field.

Impact resistance studies, however, have demonstrated that the amount of vegetation has only minor effects on surface hardness relative to that of increasing the moisture content of the soil (Table 18.2). On the other hand, increasing the height of cut may limit ball bounce and the distance of ball roll in many sports.

The well being of the turf, within limits, requires the higher cutting heights for increased photosynthetic activity, greater root and rhizome growth, greater weed control and less susceptibility to disease. It has been calculated that for every 3-mm increase in cutting height of bluegrass adds 375 m^2 of leaf surface area per 100 m^2 of a turf surface.

Raising the mowing height also reduces the soil temperature, reducing heat stress (Table 18.3), but at the same time increases the water use of the grass (Table 18.4).

Table 18.3: The relationship of mowing height to soil temperature in a Kentucky bluegrass turf.

Height of Cut	Soil Temp.@ 2.5 cm Depth
(cm)	(C)
1.9	34
2.5	32
3.8	28

(Note: Air temp @ 200 cm = 36.6, air temp. @ turf surface = 42.7)

Table 18.4: The relationship of mowing height to water use by turf-type tall fescue.

Height of Cut	Evapotranspiration
(cm)	(mm/day)
1.9	6.3
3.8	8.4
7.6	12.7

(Note: Measurements made under Nebraska conditions in June)

Even a well-managed turf may be seriously damaged when mowed following a delay in cutting due to a protracted wet spell. Raising the height of cut, followed by a step-wise lowering to the original height, can reduce the damage caused by the removal of an excessive amount of leaf material and smothering due to bunching of clippings.

Frequency of mowing is determined by how much leaf material is desirable to remove at any one time. A general rule of thumb is that not more than 1/4 to 1/3 of the leaf blade should be removed at any mowing. The less material removed, the lower the "shock" effect on the plant. The "shock" is the effect of mowing on decreasing the rate of root elongation and tiller bud development. Since root elongation has an important role in water uptake by the turf, the "shock" effect of excessive removal of tissue will also intensify water stress during periods of drought.

Mowing height and frequency depends on the species and use of the turf. Bentgrass on a bowling green requires daily mowing at six mm. In contrast bluegrass on a soccer field may require mowing at five cm every three days in early May whereas in August weekly mowing will suffice.

Types of Mowers

The mowers used in cutting turf are of three principal types — reel, rotary and flail (Figs. 18.2, 18.3).

- Reel mowers are used for precise cutting and particularly at low cutting heights such as on greens where the roll of the ball is vital. A disadvantage of a reel mower is the tendency to leave unsightly seed stems which are pushed down ahead of the reel. A reel mower cannot effectively mow grass shoots or weeds that are higher than the height of cut plus the radius of the reel. Thus a 15-cm diameter reel set to cut at five cm will not mow

Fig. 18.2: Hand operated and power operated reel mowers

Fig. 18.3: Hand operated and power operated rotary mowers.

12-cm high grass, except under very dry conditions and will not clean-cut grass more than 7.5 cm tall.

- Rotary mowers are used for general cutting and when properly set will provide a uniform surface. At heights more than 12 cm sufficient "suck" to lift the grass blades upright for an even cut can be a problem. Uncut, laid over grass in the tractor wheel marks and rows of side discharge clippings can be unsightly and damaged the turf through smothering. Rotary mowers are less expensive to maintain than reel mowers. Both reel and rotary mowers may show a wavy appearance following mowing if excessive speed is used.
- Flail mowers are best used for rough cutting or vegetation control. Cutting heights of more than 12 cm may be used and debris in the grass is not as damaging to the machine.

Sharpness is the prime consideration in the maintenance of all the types of mowers. Dull mowers leave a bruised and frayed leaf tip which turns to an unsightly grey to brown within a couple of days. Ryegrass, in particular, require a sharp mower because of the tough vascular bundles in the leaf. The cut end, with its organic exudates (bleeding), is an excellent portal of entry for pathogens, thus a clean, surgical cut is most desirable.

Mowing is a daily decision of the turf manager. A fixed mowing schedule may be administratively desirable, but the health of the turf is decided by daily, on-site assessment of the need for mowing of each field and the height of cut to be used.

CHAPTER 19

PEST MANAGEMENT

Pest management is an all-inclusive term applied to the prevention and control of infestations of weeds, insects and diseases in turf. The materials used for their control are often grouped together under the generic name of pesticides. The material required for control of a weed, an insect or a disease, however, is most often a specific chemical, targeted at a specific pest. In addition the list of available chemicals for the control of a specific pest is ever changing as research brings new products to the marketplace. Therefore this chapter will not deal with specific recommendations, but rather, the broad principles of pest management.

Since the publication of Rachel Carson's "The Silent Spring" the extensive use of chemicals for the control of diseases, insects and weeds in turf have been replaced by a common sense "use but don't abuse" approach, commonly called "Integrated Pest Management."

Specific descriptions of insect and diseases and current recommendations for control procedures are available from most provincial agricultural agencies, for example, O.M.A.F.R.A. Pub. # 162, "Turfgrass Diseases and Insect Pests" and Pub. #364, "Recommendations for Turfgrass Management."

Practices which tend to encourage vigorous turf growth are the turf manager's first line of defence against pests, whether they are weeds, insects or diseases. The practices must include fertilization, irrigation, mowing, core cultivation and overseeding with the most appropriate turf species.

Although they are important problems on golf courses and bowling greens, insects and diseases are generally not common in athletic turf. Good cultural practices such as adequate, but not excessive nitrogen and irrigation, will help to prevent infestations. Nevertheless, when they do occur the correct, early diagnosis and implementation of the necessary control strategies can eliminate most problems.

Most weeds cannot compete with healthy, dense turf. Thus those practices which encourage a dense turf will discourage weed infestation. Unfortunately intensive play on athletic fields, particularly during the slow growth periods of early spring and late fall, encourages the invasion of weed species, necessitating control strategies.

The control strategies may require the use of chemicals for control of broad leaf weeds such as dandelions, plantain, black medic, chickweed and knot weed. Chemical control is also available for crabgrass. The times of application, rates and type of chemical to use are available on the product label and in the above-mentioned publications.

A troublesome grass weed in older bluegrass stands is bent grass. At regular mowing heights for bluegrass, the bentgrass has minimal shear strength and is ripped out very easily by the running athlete. A degree of bent grass control may be obtained by vertical mowing followed by overseeding and topdressing.

One of the major problems in intensively managed, regularly irrigated turf under high nitrogen fertility for which there is limited chemical control is annual bluegrass. This weed grass is found throughout North America. The tear or shear resistance of the shallow rooted annual bluegrass is greatly inferior to the rhizomatous root system of Kentucky bluegrass. It suffers injury from low temperature, ice cover, freeze-thaw cycles, wind desiccation, and winter disease. High summer temperatures cause heat stress and it is prone to summer diseases.

Annual bluegrass is a prolific seed producer under most mowing heights. Since light promotes seed germination, initial invasions tend to occur in patches of turf that have opened up through injury. Once established, it is very competitive, producing new leaves, tillers and adventitious roots more rapidly than most competitive bluegrass cultivars.

The control of annual bluegrass is through competition from the more desirable species. Management is critical. Mow at the maximum height permitted for the sport involved. Avoid excessive nitrogen fertilization and irrigation. Irrigate only when necessary to maintain a relatively dry surface which will reduce seed germination (see Chapter 6). Maintain relatively low levels of phosphorus fertilization. Core aerate to minimize compaction and overseed with turfgrass species which are competitive in nature.

The control of annual bluegrass, for which there is no simple chemical solution, is an excellent example of a relatively new concept of pest management. The program has become known as Integrated Pest Management (IPM). It might be suggested that IPM means Intelligent Pest Management. The goal of IPM is to generate a decision making approach for the suppression of pests, whether they are weeds, insects or diseases, in effective, economical and environmentally safe ways.

The key to a successful IPM program is monitoring (scouting), identifying and recording the location and extent of the pest. The individuals who are responsible for the monitoring program must be familiar with the identification and life cycle of the pest(s) which they are dealing with. They must take, preserve, analyze and review records taken on a regular timetable.

Some suggestions for a scouting program are:

- Establish the key weeds, insects or diseases which may require control.
- Set up a suitable recording sheet which includes a check list for all relevant information, including management factors such as mowing, aeration, fertilization, irrigation, and a map with an overlying location identifying grid.
- Establish an action threshold value above which the pest becomes a problem for your particular turf situation.
- Establish a scouting pattern for walking the field and follow the same pattern consistently.
- Establish a frequency of scouting which requires a knowledge of the pest life cycle
- Have consistency in personnel conducting the scouting program.
- Evaluate the pest treatment selected to determine its degree of success and modify the scouting procedure or treatment as appropriate.

The action threshold is an important part of an IPM program. It is the frequency of occurrence of the pest in question which can be tolerated by a turf situation before control action must be taken. The action threshold is a guideline which should take into consideration the type and use of the turf. One juvenile dandelion per square meter in a soccer field may be of no concern whereas ten knotweed plants per square meter in centre field should call for treatment.

The type of control may not necessarily suggest a chemical application. Nurturing healthy turf may be the appropriate and most economical solution. Cultural control through mowing, fertilizer use, irrigation, thatch management, for example should be given first consideration. In the knotweed case compaction may be the cause which may be alleviated in the long term by core cultivation and overseeding.

Biological control is gaining importance and currently there is a great deal of research being directed toward developing control agents for turf pests. Biological control refers to the use of a predatory or pathogenic organism to control a pest. For many years the bacteria, *Baccillus thuringiensis,* have been use for the control of spruce budworm and gypsy moth. In the turf area, the research on the endophytic fungi in perennial ryegrass may become a common control measure for chinch bugs. While biological control is still in its infancy, the turf manager must be aware of these developments through the various educational programs which are available to him.

Chemical control is still an important part of any pest control program. It should be used, however, only when a pest is present in sufficient level to cause turf damage which is detrimental to the intended use of the turf. There are guidelines which can reduce the amount which needs to be applied. Some of the guidelines are:

- Apply the treatment at that time in the life cycle of the pest when it is most susceptible.
- Spot treatment when a pest is restricted to an isolated area.
- Use a properly calibrated and adjusted sprayer.
- Apply the chemical at the recommended rate under optimum weather conditions for its action.
- Select a chemical with the lowest mobility in the soil and persistence in the environment.
- Alternate chemicals to reduce the build up of pest resistance through mutations.

An IPM program for turf by any organization will evolve with time and experience. The management of the program must be committed on a long term basis to making the program work. All staff involved in turf management for an organization using IPM should be aware of the purpose of the program and continually be updated on its success and requirements. Senior administration and the public must be "on side" and realize that in extreme cases it may require such drastic action as reconstruction of a field.

CHAPTER 20

SPECIES IDENTIFICATION

The management of turf often requires that we know what species of grass we are working with. The manager may wish to know whether he is working with bluegrass, ryegrass or a fescue. His records may be misplaced. What was seeded originally may have been a mixture of species which with time has become dominated by one species. What is it?

All grasses are members of the plant family "Gramineae" which contains six sub families, 600 genera and over 7,500 species. From this widely diverse group of plants only about two dozen species, primarily the cool season grasses, are of importance in turf management. Every turf manager should have the skill to identify these few species.

Identifying Vegetative Plant Parts

The answer to the question is obtained through identifying certain vegetative plant parts. According to the characteristics of the parts the species may then be named. The plant parts are the root system, the leaf blade, the bud-shoot, the sheath, the collar, the auricle and the ligule.

- The identifying characteristic of the **root system** is the presence or absence of stolons or rhizomes. An ability to identify stolons from rhizomes is critical. Stolons are stems which grow along the soil surface or within the thatch layer. New roots and shoots emerge from the nodes on these stems. The stolons may branch at the nodes forming a network of stolons. Rhizomes are also stems, but they grow horizontally below the soil surface. When the stem approaches the soil surface light response stimulates the formation of shoots and roots at a node on the stem and a new plant results, from which one or more new rhizomes may emerge.
  Generally stolons and rhizomes are much larger in diameter than the fibrous root system. Therefore, they should not be easily confused with the general mass of roots.
- The **bud shoot** or **bud leaf** is the manner in which the newly

Figure 20.1: Illustrations of the vegetative characteristics used for grass identification.

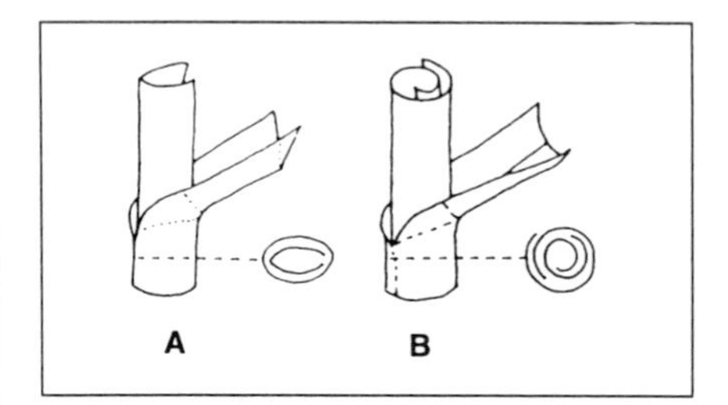

Figure 20.1.1: The Bud Shoot (A = folded, B = rolled)

Figure 20.1.2: The Leaf Tip and Surface (A = tapered, B = boat-shaped, C= ridged but not keeled, D = not ridged and keeled)

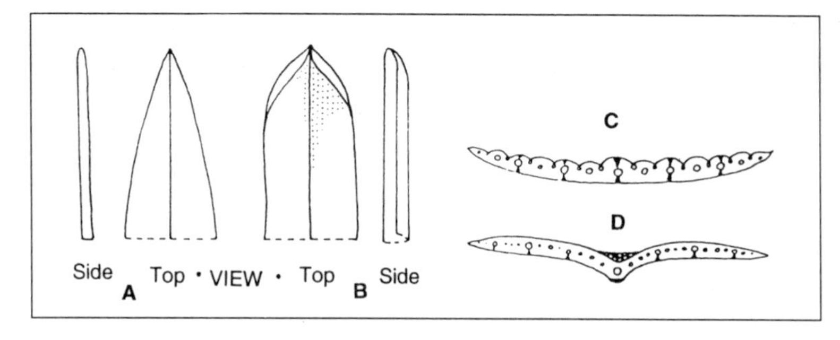

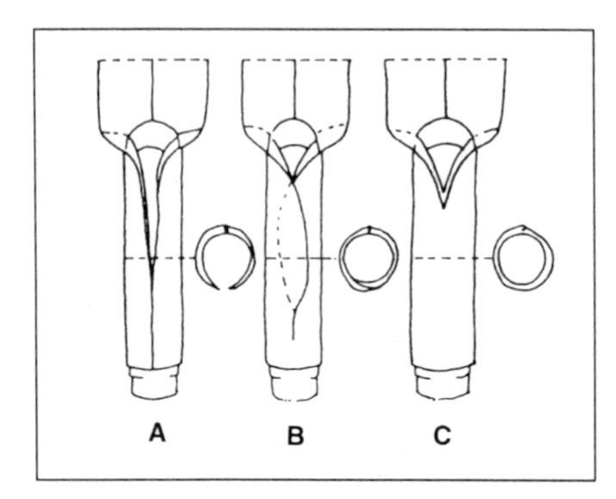

Figure 20.1.3: The Leaf Sheath (A = split, B = split with margins overlapping, C = closed)

Figure 20.1.4: The Collar (A = broad band, B = narrow band, C = divided by midrib, D = Oblique, E = Pubescent, F = ciliate, (note: A - E are back views, F is a front view)

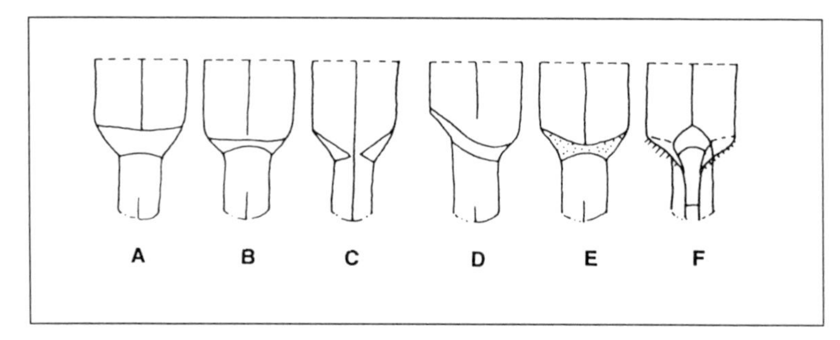

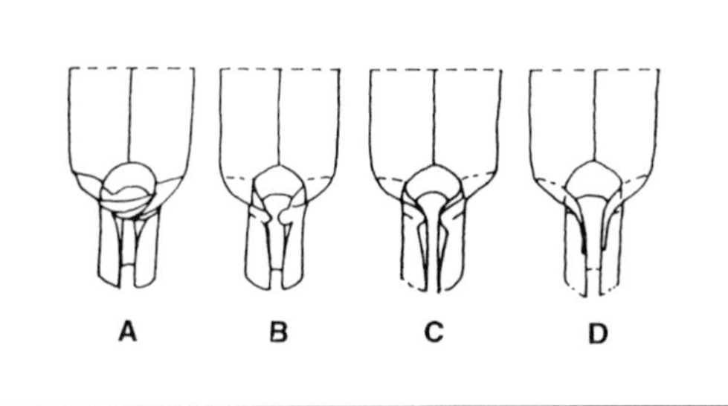

Figure 20.1.5: The Auricle
(A = claw like, B = rounded,
C = rudimentary, D = absent)

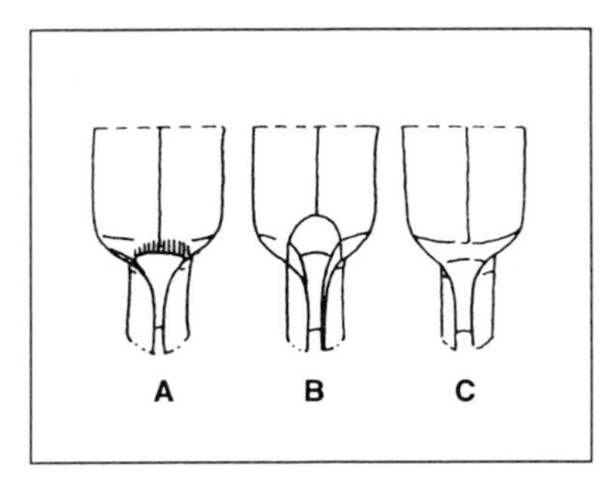

Figure 20.1.6a: The Ligule Types,
(A = fringe of hair, B = membranous,
C = absent

Figure 20.1.6b: The Ligule Margin
(A = entire, B = notched, C = lacerate,
D = ciliate)

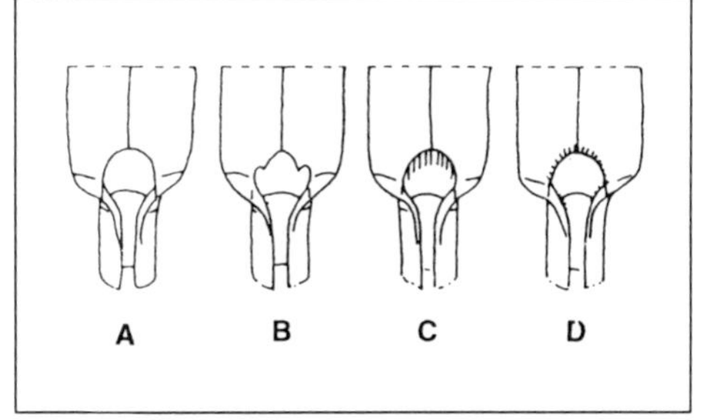

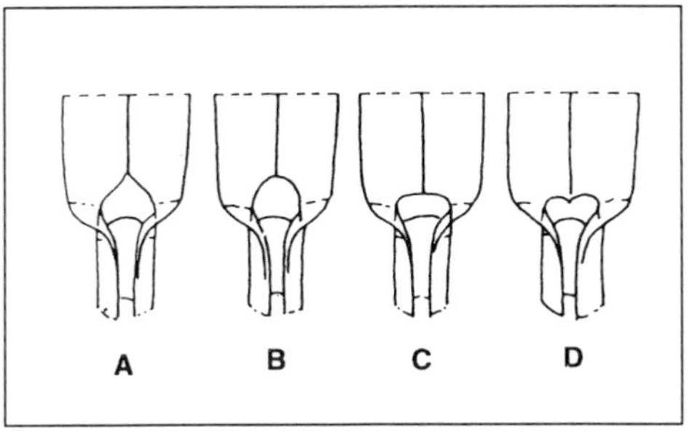

Figure 20.1.6c: The Ligule Shapes
(A = acute, B = rounded, C = truncate,
D = marginate)

emerging leaf emerges. The arrangement of the bud shoot is the basic point from which all identification of grasses commences. The bud shoot may be folded with the margins of the leaves meeting but not overlapping or it may be rolled with the margins of the leaves overlapping (Fig. 20.1).

- The **leaf blade** may be used in identifying species on the basis of the shape of the leaf tip. The differentiating characteristic is whether the leaf tip is boat -shaped or has a pointed apex (Fig. 20. 2).
- The **leaf sheath** is that tubular part of the leaf, arising at the node and closely clasping the stem or younger growing leaves upward to where the blade begins. The leaf sheath may be classified as split from the node to emergence of the blade, split at the top but tube-like near the node, or closed the entire distance from the node to where the blade emerges (Fig. 20. 3).
- The **collar** is a meristematic band or growth zone which marks the division between the blade and the sheath. The collar may be broad and prominent or narrow, continuous from one margin of the leaf to the other, or divided by a conspicuous midrib. In some species it may be higher on one side of the leaf than the other (Fig. 20. 4).
- The **auricles** are appendages projecting from the collar, one from either side. They may be absent or vary in length and shape from long and clawlike to small and rounded or rudimentary (Fig. 20. 5).
- The **ligule** is a tongue-like outgrowth at the junction of the blade and the sheath, clasping the culm or bud shoot. It may appear as a fringe of hair or as membranous tissue, or may be pubescent [covered with soft hairs] on the back (Fig. 20.6).

Turf Species

There are more than 7,500 species which belong to the family of plants called *Gramineae*. As turf grass managers in the cool temperate region, however, we need to be concerned with only 21 of these species.

Kentucky bluegrass (*Poa pratensis L.*)

Canada bluegrass (*Poa compressa L.*)

Rough bluegrass (*Poa trivialis L.*)

Annual bluegrass (*Poa annua L.*)

Supina bluegrass (*Poa supina* Schreb.)

Italian ryegrass (*Lolium multiflorum* Lam.)

Perennial ryegrass (*Lolium perenne* L.)

Tall fescue (*Festuca arundinaceae* Schreb.)

Meadow fescue (*Festuca elatior* L.)

Creeping red fescue (*Festuca rubra* L.)

Sheep's fescue (*Festuca ovina* L.)

Hard fescue (*Festuca ovina* L. subsp. *duriuscula*)

Creeping bentgrass (*Agrostis stolonifera* Huds.)

Colonial bentgrass (*Agrostis tenuis* Sibth.)

Velvet bentgrass (*Agrostis canina* L.)

Redtop (*Agrostis alba* L.)

To this list we must add three forage grasses which may invade a turf area and two weed grasses which create control problems. They are:

Brome grass (*Bromus inermis* L.)

Timothy (*Phleum pratense* L.)

Orchard grass (*Dactylis glomerata* L.)

Twitch (quack) grass (*Agropyron repens* L.)

Crabgrass (*Digitaria ischaemum* Schreb.)

Identification Key

Botanists have developed an identification key to aid in identifying plant species. A simplified key for use with turf grasses listed above is contained on the following pages. With the aid of a sharp knife and a small hand lens the plant in question is systematically examined for the several characteristics listed under identifying plant parts until a the name of the species is arrived at.

AN IDENTIFICATION KEY FOR TURF SPECIES

1.0. - Folded in the bud shoot.

1.1. - Auricle present.

1.1.1. - Lower leaf sheath reddish, back of leaf shiny. **Perennial ryegrass**

1.2. - Auricle absent.

1.2.1. - Ligule membranous.

1.2.1.1. - Blade narrow, prominently ridged on upper surface.

1.2.1.1.1. - Ligule less than 0.5 mm or absent, sheath split, leaves waxy, plant tufted. **Sheep fescue**

1.2.1.1.2. - Ligule over 0.5 mm, sheath closed, leaves not waxy, plant not tufted. **Red fescue**

1.2.2. - Ligule absent to very short.

1.2.2.1. Without rhizomes.

1.2.2.1.1. - Sheath keeled or with prominent ridge like a boat keel running down base of leaf which gradually tapers to apex. **Canada bluegrass**

1.2.2.2. - With rhizomes.

1.2.2.2.1. - Sheath not keeled,leaf parallel sided, with abruptly pointed and boat shaped tip. **Kentucky bluegrass**

1.2.3. - Ligule rounded or pointed, more than 1.0 mm long.

1.2.3.1. - With stolons.

1.2.3.1.1. - Tapered and boat shaped leaf tip, sheath rough, blade glossy under surface. **Rough bluegrass**

1.2.3.2. - Without stolons.

1.2.3.2.1. - Parallel side leaf with tip abruptly pointed and boat shaped. **Annual bluegrass**

1.2.3.2.2. - Leaf blade wide and taper pointed, stem base flattened. **Orchardgrass**

2.0. - Rolled in the bud shoot.

2.1. - Auricles present.

2.1.1. - Auricle blunt to claw like and with minute marginal hairs, very shiny underside, strongly ribbed upper side of leaf. **Tall fescue**

2.1.2. - Auricles without marginal hairs, leaf soft and less shiny, margin of leaf harsh or slightly rough or jagged to finger when slid lengthwise down edge near leaf base. **Meadow fescue**

2.1.3. - Margin of leaf smooth, auricle small, rarely reaching 1/4 distance around stem, ligule over 1 mm. **Italian ryegrass**

2.1.4. - Sheath, collar, and blade with short soft hairs, rhizomes prominent which are white and pointed. **Quack grass**

2.2. - Auricles absent.

2.2.1. - Ligule membranous.

2.2.1.1. - Leaf sheath closed, its margins united except for a small V-shaped notch near the collar, leaf sheath and blade hairless, "W'" marking of wrinkled tissue near middle of leaf, rhizomes present. **Bromegrass**

2.2.1.2. - Leaf sheath split, hairless and compressed with ridge or keel down the back. **Crabgrass**

2.2.2. - Ligule 1.5 mm or longer with prominent notch on either side, enlarged or bulbous base to stem. **Timothy**

2.2.2.1. - Ligule without notch, rhizomes present. **Redtop**

2.2.2.2. - Ligule shorter than 1.5 mm, rhizomes slender and short. **Colonial bentgrass**

2.2.2.3. - Stolons present. **Creeping bentgrass**

2.2.2.4. - Stolons present, ligule tends to be pointed. **Velvet bentgrass**

It is important to remember that the key is based on contrasting pairs of statements. If the first statement is not true then you move on to the next statement at the same level in the key.

Let us take an example. The first characteristic listed in the key is the bud shoot. As there are only two possibilities the first step is to determine whether the sample is folded in the bud shoot or rolled in the bud shoot. Let us assume that it is folded (1.0). The alternative statement is rolled in the bud shoot (2.0.). The second step is to determine whether the sample has auricles. Let us assume that it does not (1.2.). The third step is to examine the shape of the ligule. Let us assume that a ligule is hard to see or absent (1.2.2). Further examination reveals the plants have very prominent rhizomes (1.2.2.2.) and for confirmation that the leaves are not tapered but parallel sided and boat shaped at the tip. Following these observations through the key reveals that the plant you have examined is Kentucky bluegrass.

Practice is necessary to develop skills in using the key. Some initial short cuts can often save time, such as to examine the plant for rhizomes or stolons. Broad leaf species will often turn out to be quack grass or forage grasses. Crab grass in August can easily be identified by its particular seed head, even at less than two inch mowing.

CHAPTER 21

THE BLUEGRASSES

The grass species most common to the cool season, sub-humid to arid climates of Canada for sports turf and fairways is Kentucky bluegrass.

Kentucky bluegrass was introduced into North America from Europe by the early settlers, probably as livestock feed during the ocean voyages or as mattress padding. The origin of the name "Kentucky" is probably from Kentucky where seed was first harvested from pasture stands. The medium textured soils of Kentucky derived from limestone and high in phosphorus would have been favourable to the growth of this popular turfgrass species.

The Bluegrass Family

Of the more than 200 *Poa* species in the world, there are only five bluegrass or *Poa* species which are commonly found in turf. While Kentucky bluegrass (*Poa pratensis L.*) is the most important and desirable species, a second species, Canada bluegrass or *Poa compressa L.*, finds use in restoration of drought susceptible, low fertility areas. It forms an open, stemy turf which lacks the strong, rhizomatous nature of Kentucky bluegrass. As a result it is of little value for sports fields.

Rough bluegrass, *Poa trivialis L.*, is a stoloniferous species which also has limited use because it lacks heat and drought tolerance, turning brown during midsummer stress periods. The above ground stolons do not provide the wear resistance of Kentucky bluegrass. It does, however, have excellent cold tolerance making it worthy of consideration in areas where winter survival of Kentucky bluegrass is a problem.

The renegade of the bluegrass species is the widely distributed annual bluegrass, *Poa annua* L. This species is commonly considered a weed grass due to its low tolerance to wear, heat, drought and cold stress. The species is a prolific seed producer, particularly during the cool, moist spring, and spreads by the seed carried on mowing equipment and footwear. As many as 10 viable seeds per square cm have been reported in golf greens. The seeds do not have a dormancy period. Thus the seed may germinate within days of hitting the soil surface. Poa annua also spreads by stolons and is shallow rooted; factors which reduce its wear tolerance.

The fifth species of bluegrass is a recent introduction from Europe, *Poa sapina* Schrad. It appears to be related to annual bluegrass and has received considerable attention in Europe for sports fields. Initial information on the species indicates that while slow to develop during the seedling year it becomes quite aggressive in later years. Its aggressiveness is in part due to heavy seed production and early season growth. It is reported to prevent or inhibit the spread of annual bluegrass when managed with high nitrogen and water.

Kentucky Bluegrass Advantages

The most significant advantage of Kentucky bluegrass for sports fields is that in addition to normal tiller formation it has the ability to spread by means of rhizomes from which new plants develop to colonize bare areas, giving it great recuperative potential. Thus, under good growing conditions the stand heals rapidly following injury. The interlocking network of rhizomes and roots within the soil, rather than above the soil surface as is the case with stolon-forming *Poa* species, significantly enhances the wear resistance of Kentucky bluegrass.

It has been estimated that a single Kentucky bluegrass plant can produce six to 18 meters of rhizomes from the original shoot between mid-June and mid-November. Each node on the rhizome is capable of initiating a new shoot and root system. It is this rhizome system which makes Kentucky bluegrass the preferred species for sports fields.

Additional advantages of Kentucky bluegrass are that it performs well under a wide variety of soil conditions, showing good heat and drought tolerance and that it is winter hardy. Under high temperatures and/or water restrictions, however, Kentucky bluegrass will enter a period of slow growth, often referred to as summer dormancy. With the return of fall rains the turf will resume normal growth in about three weeks.

The optimum temperature for top growth is 21 - 24 C, and optimum root growth occurs at 15 C and continues below 4.5 C, a factor favouring nitrogen uptake from late fall fertilization. It is interesting to note that higher temperatures stimulate the emergence above the soil surface of growing points of new tillers from nodes on rhizomes whereas lower temperatures enhance the elongation of the rhizomes.

Kentucky bluegrass has a medium tolerance to low soil oxygen levels caused by poor drainage or compaction. It is a salt sensitive grass. Conductivities due to salts in excess of four millimhos are known to be harmful. It prefers a pH in the range of 6.0 to 7.0 but will grow very satisfactorily at pH a 7.5 which exists on many sport facilities in Canada.

Kentucky Bluegrass Disadvantages

Kentucky bluegrass is slow to germinate, generally requiring two to three weeks to emerge. Its use for the quick repair of sports field turf, therefore, is limited. An athletic field seeded to bluegrass will require at least a year to be sufficiently mature to stand intensive play. Light is required for gemination of all bluegrass species. Although the intensity of light is very low, seed buried below 2 - 5 mm may never emerge.

In a rating of shade tolerance, bluegrass is considered poor in relationship to perennial ryegrass, bentgrass and fine fescues. When the shade is caused by trees, the problem of shade tolerance is compounded by the demand of the tree for water and nutrients.

Ice damage is a problem throughout Canada. Kentucky bluegrass is intermediate between bentgrass and annual bluegrass in its tolerance to ice sheet injury with bentgrass being the most tolerant. Kentucky bluegrass will tolerate up to 50 days of ice cover (skating rinks) without damage if adequate drainage exists to remove water formed during thaws. A snow layer between the ice and the turf significantly reduces the ice damage. Frost heaving may be a serious problem for late fall seeded bluegrass. The corrective measure for most winter injury is good drainage.

Kentucky bluegrass is a relatively heavy thatch former. While thatch adds resiliency to turf, an excessive thatch contributes to disease problems. Topdressing or coring practices may have to be considered where thatch buildup under bluegrass becomes a problem.

Cultural Practices

The recommended seeding rate for Kentucky bluegrass is 1.0 - 2.0 kg/100 m^2. This seeding rate will provide 4.8 to 9.6 million seeds per 100 m^2; about five seeds per square centimetre.

There are more than three dozen cultivars of Kentucky bluegrass available for use in Canada. Generally a blend of two or more cultivars is preferred to capitalize on the slightly different attributes of each individual cultivar.

Kentucky bluegrass is responsive to phosphorus fertilization, particularly during the establishment period. A high rating on the phosphorus soil test is desirable during this period. Where the initial level of phosphorus fertility is high and clippings are not removed minimal phosphorus fertilization may be required in future years.

Kentucky bluegrass has a medium demand for nitrogen fertilization. Generally .25 to .75 kg N/100 m^2 per growing month is required for good growth, however, the rates should be adjusted according to the turf manager experiences in the colour and density from nitrogen applications. Potassium should be applied according to the rate suggested by a soil test. Alternatively a rough guideline is one kg of K_2O for every two kg of nitrogen.

Disease on sports field turf is generally not a problem. Helminthosporium leaf spot, Fusarim patch (pink snow mold) and Typhula blight (grey snow mold) may be a problem under some conditions but chemical treatment is seldom necessary.

In recent years insect damage to sports fields from chinch bug and European chafer has become a problem in Ontario and Quebec. The insects drastically damage the root system which reduces the wear resistance of the turf. Chemical control may be necessary where the grub population warrants.

The optimum cutting height for Kentucky bluegrass is 2.5 to 5 cm, with the higher height preferred for sports fields. Cultivars have been developed for lower mowing heights for use on golf fairways, but greater wear tolerance has not been shown to be associated with the lower mowing height.

CHAPTER 22

THE RYEGRASSES

The Ryegrass Family

There are about ten species of ryegrass which have been botanically identified, but only two are commonly used in the turfgrass industry. Italian ryegrass (*Lolium multiflorum* Lam.), sometimes referred to as annual ryegrass due to the predominately annual growth habit, is a native of the Mediterranean regions of Europe. It is noted for its rapid germination rate and hence may be used where rapid cover is desired. The annual nature and low cold tolerance of the species limit its use for sports turf in Canada. Under more tropical environments annual ryegrass has found a place in overseeding dormant tropical grasses for winter play.

On the other hand, perennial ryegrass (*Lolium perenne* L.), sometimes referred to as English ryegrass has a world wide reputation as a premier grass for sports turf use. The reputation has been gained through the superior wear resistance of the grass. It originated in the temperate areas of Asia and North Africa. Although a bunch type grass without the colonizing ability of bluegrass with its rhizomes, ryegrass may provide a dense, high wear resistant turf when grown in temperate climates under high fertility and adequate water. Hence it remains the preferred sports field grass in Europe.

Ryegrass was first developed as a pasture grass which would withstand close grazing. It was also found to have a superior ability to produce meat and milk. The early settlers in New Zealand fell and burnt the forest, then threw ryegrass seed in the ashes to develop one of the greatest introduced grazing environments in the world for the production of meat, milk and wool.

Ryegrass Advantages

The major advantage of ryegrass is the wear-resistant qualities of the ryegrass leaf. The wear resistance is derived from the extremely tough, fibrous vascular bundles in the leaves. While this advantage increases the wear ability of the leaf, it means ryegrass is more difficult to mow than other species of turfgrass. A whitish appearance, due to shredded, mutilated leaves, may be observed if the mower becomes dull.

A second advantage of ryegrass is the relatively rapid germination and emergence rate. Under favourable temperature conditions of 12 - 25 C, ryegrass will emerge in five to eight days. Thus, ryegrass is the preferred species for overseeding in the late spring or late fall when soil temperatures may be low. In overseeding operations rapid germination of the ryegrass increases its competition potential with weed species, such as annual bluegrass, which may also be germinating. On the other hand, because of the rapid establishment, ryegrass can be excessively competitive in mixtures with other species, resulting in poor establishment of the preferred species, usually Kentucky bluegrass.

Since ryegrass is a bunch grass thatch accumulation is seldom a problem. Thus, topdressing programs for thatch control are seldom required on sports fields with a high content of ryegrass.

Ryegrass will perform well under a wide variety of soil conditions, including the heavy textured soils. It has fair to good tolerance to poor drainage and compaction. The latter advantage makes the species a popular choice for reseeding goalmouth and centre field areas, but it does not correct the underlying problem and will not perform as well as if the soil was less dense. Best performance is obtained on neutral soils, however, it will tolerate slightly acidic soils. Drought tolerance is medium. Its adaptation to shade, relative to bluegrass, is good.

Ryegrass Disadvantages

A major disadvantage of ryegrass is the bunch-type growth habit. It lacks the rhizomes of Kentucky bluegrass or the stolons of bentgrass which enable them to colonize bare areas. Recovery from winter kill or other stress factors is poor and overseeding becomes essential. Ryegrass will also become stemy during late spring when numerous reproductive tillers are formed. The stems will resist mowing by reel mowers giving the sports field a ragged appearance.

As a result of the bunch grass growth habit, ryegrass will appear as clumps if it becomes thin. Therefore, a regular overseeding program should be practiced to maintain a thick stand. Generally the overseeding program can be carried out with little or no site preparation unless soil leveling is required.

A second disadvantage is the lack of cold tolerance. More recent cultivar introductions of turf type perennial ryegrass, however, have increase cold tolerance. Unless good snow cover can be assured in areas with severe winters, winter kill can be a serious problem.

Ryegrass is susceptible to leaf rusts. In August and early September rust can reduce the vigour and quality of pure ryegrass stands growing at low levels of nitrogen fertilization and without irrigation. Under sports field condition other diseases seldom become a problem with ryegrass.

Ryegrass is not tolerant of close mowing. A height of five to seven cm is preferred, although the higher mowing height may create problems obtaining a clean cut. Because of the tough nature of the leaf and the stems which appear in late spring, a rotary mower may produce a superior quality turf in comparison to a reel mower.

Cultural Practices

Satisfactory quality of ryegrass turf may be maintained with medium fertility which involves 0.25 - 0.75 kg N/100 m^2 per growing month. The higher rate may be necessary for high use fields on which midfield and goalmouth wear can be more intensive. Phosphorus and potassium requirements are similar to those of other species.

Turf-type perennial ryegrass varieties are recommended for Southern Ontario, lower mainland B.C. and Vancouver Island, and the coastal areas of the maritime provinces. Relative to bluegrass, perennial ryegrass is a large seed. Therefore the recommended seeding rate is 2.0 - 4.0 kg seed/100 m^2.

CHAPTER 23

THE FESCUES

A renewed interest in the fescues has occurred in recent years as a cool season turf species with the advent of turf-type cultivars of tall fescue. The interest has been sparked by the ability of some members of the fescue family to continue to provide an acceptable appearance when under stress, such as drought or heat.

Tall fescue will tolerate the soil conditions and maintenance of a poor sports field, but a good sports field will not tolerate tall fescue.

The Fescue Family

The fescues originated in Europe, but today are common throughout the world.

While there are approximately 100 fescue species, only six are considered of any value for turf. The six are divided into two groups on the basis of leaf texture or width: the course fescues and the fine fescues.

The course fescues are tall fescue (*Festuca arundinaceae* Schreb.) and meadow fescue (*Festuca elatior* L.). The fine fescues are creeping red fescue (*Festuca rubra* L.), Chewings fescue (*Festuca rubra* L. *commutata*), sheep fescue (*Festuca ovina* L. subsp. *ovina*) and hard fescue (*Festuca ovina* L. subsp. *duriuscula).*

As the name suggests the course fescues are characterized by a relatively broad, wear resistant leaf and deep rooting. As a result they are relatively tolerant to stress, especially to drought and heat. Stands of tall fescue, however, tend to grow in clumps, particularly in thin stands, because it is a bunch grass which expands by tiller formation at the edge of a wide crown. Meadow fescue is a relatively short-lived, bunch grass which has some tolerance to poor drainage, but is seldom considered for sports field mixtures.

Under heavy wear, mixed stands of tall fescue with spreading rhizomatous species such as Kentucky bluegrass, tend to isolate the bunch grass into unsightly clumps. A pure tall fescue stand, overseeded with bluegrass for renovation purposes, will quickly become an unsightly rough turf.

While originally developed as a pasture species for the transition zone between cool season and warm season grasses, recent cultivar selections have generated turfgrass cultivars of tall fescue which have a finer leaf that is visually more acceptable.

The fine fescues are generally represented by creeping red fescue, however, there are subtle differences between the various subspecies. Creeping red fescue has short, slender rhizomes and is thus capable of colonizing bare areas. In contrast Chewings fescue does not have rhizomes. Sheeps fescue, also a bunch grass, has the ability to survive under extreme drought conditions of sandy or gravelly soils. Hard fescue, likewise a bunch grass, is the coarsest of the fine fescues.

Fescue Advantages

The major advantage of the turf-type tall fescue cultivars is their tolerance to stress, whether it is from drought, heat, fertility or wear. During periods of heat or drought stress the leaves retain their colour and rigidity better than most other turf grasses. The coarse mature of the leaves imparts a relatively high degree of wear tolerance into tall fescue. Therefore it has been suggested for sports fields where minimum maintenance is to be used.

The second advantage of turf-type tall fescues is the recent interest in endophyte alkaloid production which imparts a degree of insect resistance to the tall fescue.

Due to the dark green colour of the leaf, tall fescue appears to tolerate low fertility and acid pH better than other turf species. Nevertheless, its growth performance is best with a soil pH of 5.5 to 6.5 and medium to high fertility. An advantage for other uses, such as drainage channels, is its tolerance to wet conditions and ability to survive periods of submersion.

Tall fescue emerges rapidly which makes it a desirable species for overseeding areas where the turf has been lost due to excessive wear.

Meadow fescue has many of the same advantages as tall fescue, but in addition it has a brighter leaf, a finer textured leaf and greater shade tolerance. It is seldom used in sports field mixtures in North America, but is more compatible than tall fescue in mixes with Kentucky bluegrass.

The main advantage of the fine fescues is the fine textured leaf. The principle species used for turf is creeping red fescue, so named from the extravaginal type of root development and occurrence of thin, short rhizomes. It also has a fibrous and extremely dense root system.

Creeping red fescue has the greatest shade tolerance of the cool season turf species. Shoot density under shaded conditions, however, is less than in full sun. Nevertheless, under full sun conditions a mixture of mixture of bluegrass and red fescue will be dominated by the bluegrass. It has good drought tolerance but does not tolerate poorly drained soils.

Creeping red fescue has received some favour as grass cover for areas which are not mowed due to its relatively attractive seed head, low growing habit and dense stand when fertilized with a moderate level of nitrogen.

The primary advantage of Chewings fescue is its tolerance to acidic soils. Its other attributes are similar to red fescue.

The principal advantage of sheeps fescue is the high degree of drought tolerance. It is also a particularly long-live perennial.

Fescue Disadvantages

With the exception of creeping red fescue the main disadvantage of the fescues is their bunch type habit of growth. Unless a very dense stand is maintained, the advantage associated with wear quality of fescues is lost on sports fields. Furthermore when stands become thin and overseeded with bluegrass the overall appearance of the field deteriorates due to the surviving course clumps of tall fescue.

To maintain a desirable turf of tall fescue an intense overseeding program is required. Seed germination is sufficiently rapid to allow the overseeding to be successful even during period of field use.

Tall fescues do not have the cold tolerance of the bluegrasses. The lack of cold tolerance adds to the rate of thinning of the stand and the tendency to form a clumpy, undesirable turf within a few years of seeding.

Due to the very fine nature of the leaf and the tendency to lie over or lodge, the fine fescues are difficult to mow unless maintained at a relatively low mowing height of less than 5.0 cm.

Cultural Practices

Good performance of fescues is obtained with medium levels of nitrogen. In fact the red fescues may decline in quality with high levels of nitrogen. Phosphorus and potassium requirements are similar to other turf species.

With the exception of the fine fescues cutting at less 5.0 cm will encourage the clumpy growth habit of the fescues.

While tolerant of adverse soil conditions best performance is obtained where good soil conditions of porosity, drainage, neutral pH and fertility are maintained.

Seed mixtures of tall fescue and perennial ryegrass should be (by weight) 50% ryegrass:50% fescue. With bluegrass the mixture should be 20% bluegrass:80% fescue.

CHAPTER 24

THE BENTGRASSES

The bentgrasses originated in Europe and were introduced to North America during colonial times. Today they are found wherever there are golf greens in the cool temperate climates.

Bentgrass is the preferred turf species where true ball roll is the top priority for the turf surface. Therefore bentgrass will be found on all golf and bowling greens in the cool temperate climates.

The Bentgrass Family

Although there are at least 100 species of grasses listed in the genus *Agrostis* there is only four species of bentgrass used in the turf industry. The most common is creeping bentgrass (*Agrostis palustris* Huds or *A. stolonifera)*. The others are red-top (*Agrostis alba* L.), velvet bentgrass (*Agrostis canina* L.) and Colonial bentgrass (*Agrostis tenuis* Sibth.). The latter are also known as browntop in the U.K. and New Zealand.

The bentgrasses are used for intensively managed areas where dense surfaces are required. Due to the predominately prostrate growth habit, the bentgrasses are the most tolerant of the cool season grasses to continued close mowing, often as low as three mm. Under this mowing regime the bentgrasses can form a fine textured, dense, uniform, high quality turf, ideally suited for true ball roll on golf and bowling greens.

All of the bentgrasses are characterized by being fine leaved, cool-season, perennial species. Colonial bentgrass and red top are primarily rhizomatous species, that is, they spread by means of underground stems. In contrast velvet bent and creeping bentgrass are stoloniferous species that have horizontal stems creeping above the soil surface.

The species are generally propagated by seed, however, vegetative propagation is feasible. As a result Toronto C-15, which originated at the Toronto Golf Club in Long Branch became very popular throughout the North East and Mid-Western U.S., and was propagated by stolons or sod moved to new golf greens. The more disease resistant varieties available today, however, are all propagated by seed. The standard variety of creeping bentgrass, against which all other improved varieties are rated today is Penncross that was released by Penn State University in 1954.

Bentgrass Advantages

As intimated above the main advantage of the bentgrass is its ability to maintain a dense turf under very low mowing heights. The advantage arises from the very short lower internodes. Creeping bentgrass is the superior species in this regard where mowing heights of five mm or less is required. Colonial bent is less tolerant to low mowing heights and tends to eventually form a mottled, patchy appearance due to segregation into off-type clones. Velvet bent also is less desirable for use at low mowing situations due to heavy thatch formation and the resulting scalping that may occur. The heavy thatch accumulation is due to a relatively slow rate of decomposition of root and stolon material. Colonial bent also has thatch accumulation problems requiring more frequent topdressing than creeping bent grass.

A second, related advantage is the recuperative ability from injury. The recuperative ability of the species of bent is largely related to their means of spreading. Creeping bent has the most vigorous stolon system, hence the most rapid recovery from divots or bare areas caused by disease or winter injury. On the other hand colonial bent and velvet bent spread by rhizomes or short, slow growing stolons whereas red top has rhizomes only, giving them slower recuperative ability.

A third advantage of the bent grasses is their tolerance to winter injury. Creeping bentgrass is one of the most winter hardy of the cool season turf species. Colonial bent has slightly less cold tolerance and red top has even less tolerance; to the degree it is sometimes considered a short-lived perennial.

The bentgrasses are also reported to have good tolerance to poor soil conditions, low pH soils, having drought tolerance and being tolerant of poor fertility. While these attributes may be true, optimum performance of the species only occurs where drainage, water, and fertility are enhanced.

Red tops' adaptation to coarse textured, low fertility conditions gives the species a niche in the low maintenance and erosion control situations. The reddish hue of the inflorescence provides an added aesthetic appeal.

Bentgrass Disadvantages

The bentgrasses tend to be very prone to disease. Fusarium patch, Sclerotinia dollar spot, Helminthosporium and many others, such that a preventive fungicide program is often used when disease problems are anticipated. Recognition of the particular disease and its control requires a high degree of management skills and costly chemicals.

Creeping bentgrass, and to a lesser degree colonial bentgrass, has little tolerance to compaction that is often a problem on greens. Furthermore the rooting system tends to be shallow and lacks the toughness required to withstand the tearing action of the player's cleats.

Water stress may be a problem where bentgrasses are produced on freely draining, coarse textured rooting zones. The irrigation demand arises from the relatively shallow root system of the bent grasses. While creeping and colonial bentgrass has a medium to good level of heat tolerance, mid day syringing is often necessary under conditions of high evapotranspiration.

Creeping bentgrass and colonial bentgrass are subject to root injury from phenoxy herbicides such as 2,4-D.

Whereas creeping bentgrass, colonial bentgrass and red top have low to medium shade tolerance, velvet bentgrass may be grown under conditions of partial shade.

Cultural Practices

When used on a playing surface the bentgrasses demand a relatively high fertility level, particularly nitrogen. Yearly applications of up to 4.0 kg N/100 m^2, split into six to eight applications may be required. Consideration should be given to using at least 50% of the nitrogen as a slow release carrier to avoid foliar burn. Uneven coverage at low rates may result in a "freckling" of the turf. Higher levels of phosphorus and potassium are required than for normal sports fields.

Mowing bentgrass is a daily operation. The low mowing height requires a special greens mower which should be well maintained and sharp. The greens mower should be equipped with a comb to prevent grain from developing in the turf which will influence the ball roll. Grain may also be avoided by alternating the direction of mowing.

Topdressing for thatch control and to level the surface is an important practice on bentgrass. At the low cutting height used on bentgrass thatch accumulation may result in unsightly scalping that will also distract from a true ball roll.

Verticutting may also be used for thatch control. In addition vertical mowing cut the stolons, thus promoting juvenile shoot development and rooting at the nodes on the stolons.

Compaction control is essential for good growth of creeping bentgrass. The problem arises where greens are constructed from local soils or where specifications for materials selection for U.S.G.A. type greens are not followed. Hollow tyne aerification with topdressing will not only relieves the compaction problem, but will also provide thatch control.

Index

The Sports Turf Association

acknowledges the generous support of